The Open University

Mathematics: A Second Level Course

Linear Mathematics

Unit 12 LINEAR FUNCTIONALS AND DUALITY
Unit 13 SYSTEMS OF DIFFERENTIAL EQUATIONS

Prepared by the Linear Mathematics Course Team

18-9-72

The Open University Press

The Open University Press Walton Hall Bletchley Bucks.

First published 1972
Copyright © 1972 The Open University

Designed by the Media Development Group of the Open University.

Printed in Great Britain by
Martin Cadbury Printing Group

SBN 335 01103 9

This text forms part of the correspondence element of an Open University
Second Level Course. The complete list of units in the course is given at the end of
this text.

For general availability of supporting material referred to in this text, please
write to the Director of Marketing, The Open University, Walton Hall, Bletchley,
Buckinghamshire.

Further information on Open University courses may be obtained from the
Admissions Office, The Open University, P.O. Box 48, Bletchley, Buckinghamshire.

Unit 12 Linear Functions and Duality

Contents

Set Books

D. L. Kreider, R. G. Kuller, D. R. Ostberg and F. W. Perkins, *An Introduction to Linear Analysis* (Addison-Wesley, 1966).

E. D. Nering, *Linear Algebra and Matrix Theory* (John Wiley, 1970).

It is essential to have these books; the course is based on them and will not make sense without them.

Conventions

Before working through this correspondence text make sure you have read *A Guide to the Linear Mathematics Course*. Of the typographical conventions given in the Guide the following are the most important.

The set books are referred to as :

K for *An Introduction to Linear Analysis*
N for *Linear Algebra and Matrix Theory*

All starred items in the summaries are examinable.

References to the Open University Mathematics Foundation Course Units (The Open University Press, 1971) take the form *Unit M100 3, Operations and Morphisms*.

12.0 INTRODUCTION

This unit introduces you to two important mathematical concepts, *linear functionals* and *duality*. The first of these concepts is quite easy to understand—in fact, as you will see, a linear functional is just a special case of a linear transformation. Duality, however, is less concrete. Instead of being a rigidly defined mathematical *object*, it is a series of related *properties* possessed by various kinds of mathematical object. It is an idea that mathematicians have been aware of for a very long time, but it has been given a rigorous mathematical expression only as recently as 1945. Duality has played a very important part in the recent development of higher mathematics, and if you continue with mathematics to a higher level, you may study areas in pure mathematics which have been developed with its help. But in this unit, the main aim is to introduce you to the idea of duality in the specific context of linear functionals.

The portion of Nering covered in this unit is quite small—Sections 1 and 2, the last paragraph of Section 3, and part of Section 4, of **N** Chapter IV. It is written in a very condensed style, even for Nering, and we would suggest that, in this case, you should work through the appropriate section of **N** as part of the summary of each section of this text.

By a linear *functional* we mean simply a linear transformation whose codomain is whatever field of scalars we are working with (i.e. normally the field R). There are many examples of such transformations. One is the transformation from R^2 to R which maps each ordered pair (x, y) in the domain R^2 to its first member x; another is the transformation from $C[0, 1]$ (the set of all continuous real-valued functions with domain $[0, 1]$) to R which maps each function f in $C[0, 1]$ to its definite integral $\int_0^1 f$. Linear functionals also arise very naturally whenever we want to solve a system of algebraic equations; for example, in the system

$$2x + y = 5$$
$$2x - 3y = 1$$

the left-hand side of the first equation can be written $\phi(x, y) = 5$, where ϕ is the linear functional that maps (x, y) to $2x + y$. They also arise naturally in linear programming* problems. Suppose, for example, that you wanted to devise a diet, consisting, say, of a apples per week, b bananas, c cabbages and so on, which would provide the necessary amounts of protein, fat, carbohydrate and the various vitamins, at the minimum cost. The cost of a week's supply of food is then

$$Aa + Bb + Cc + \cdots$$

where A is the price of an apple, B that of a banana and so on, and this can be written $\phi(a, b, c, \ldots)$ where ϕ is the linear functional

$$(a, b, c, \ldots) \longmapsto Aa + Bb + Cc + \cdots$$

Mathematically, the problem of devising this diet is the same as that of finding the minimum value of the linear functional ϕ subject to certain conditions on $(a, b, c \ldots)$ which represent the conditions that the diet contains enough protein, enough fat, etc., and that all the quantities of food must be greater than or equal to 0. The linear functional itself gives a mathematical representation of the price structure within which the diet is being worked out. For our problem it contains exactly the same information as a price list giving the numbers $[A, B, C, \ldots]$, which you might see in a greengrocer's shop. (The reason why we use *square* brackets here will be explained later in the unit.)

---

* Linear programming is the subject of *Unit 18* of this course.

5

The idea of duality arises in roughly the following way. We have just seen that the price list $[A, B, C, \ldots]$ corresponds to a linear functional ϕ, whose domain is the set of all possible shopping lists $(a, b, c, \ldots)$; this functional represents the way the price list affects the customer, who wants to know how her total food bill depends on what she decides to buy. But from the greengrocer's point of view, things look rather different. He wants to know whether he can increase his profit by altering the price list, and so one of the things he is interested in is how the total cost of a given shopping list depends on his prices. In other words, he thinks of the customer's shopping list as determining a function whose domain is the set of all the price lists he might use:

$$\psi : [A, B, C, \ldots] \longmapsto Aa + Bb + Cc + \cdots$$

This is another linear functional.

Mathematically, these two viewpoints give rise to two vector spaces: the customer's space, in which the shopping list is thought of as a vector and the price list as a linear functional, and the greengrocer's space in which the price list is thought of as a vector, and the shopping list as a linear functional. These two spaces are said to be *dual* vector spaces. This dual point of view turns out to be very useful in linear programming problems, such as the diet problem mentioned above. (Actually, shopping lists such as these do not strictly speaking form vector spaces over R, because, for example, if α is in the space then $-\alpha$ is not. Nevertheless, they serve to make the mathematical point we are interested in.)

12.1 LINEAR FUNCTIONALS

12.1.1 The Definition of a Linear Functional

The object of this sub-section is to make precise the mathematical definition of a linear functional. As we said in the Introduction to the unit, a linear functional is simply a linear transformation whose codomain is the field of scalars with which we are working.

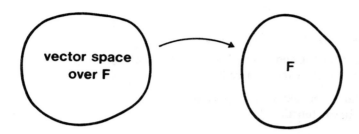

But this implies that we are considering the field of scalars to be a vector space over itself, since the codomain of a linear transformation is a vector space. Can we do this?

Let us be specific about this. We know that R^2, R^3, and so on, are vector spaces, with bases $\{(1, 0), (0, 1)\}$ (for R^2), $\{(1, 0, 0), (0, 1, 0), (0, 0, 1)\}$ (for R^3), and so on. It would be very odd indeed if we could not tack R itself (i.e. R^1) on to the beginning of this series of vector spaces, and use the single element 1 of R as a basis. We can indeed do this*; all the axioms of addition and scalar multiplication work if we regard the set of "vectors" in the vector space as just a copy of the set of "scalars". The operation of "scalar multiplication" of a "vector" α by a "scalar" b simply results in the element $b\alpha$, which is perfectly well defined in terms of the multiplication operation in R. Conceptually, this multiplication should not be thought of as the multiplication of two vectors in the "vector space" copy of R, but rather as the result of multiplying a "vector" in R by a "scalar" in R.

For example, if we agree to embolden the elements of R when they are acting as *vectors*, then

$$\mathbf{2} + \mathbf{3} = \mathbf{5}$$
$$\mathbf{2}3 \quad = \mathbf{6} \qquad \text{(scalar multiplication of a vector),}$$
$$2 \cdot 3 \quad = 6 \qquad \text{(multiplication within the field of scalars).}$$

In practice, it is not necessary to keep the two roles of R separate; this does not, after all, affect the results of any calculations. In general, for any field F, the above argument applies word for word, and we can define a linear functional as follows.

Definition

If V is a vector space over a field F, then a *linear functional* on V is a function ϕ with domain V and codomain F, such that ϕ is a linear transformation, i.e.

$$\phi(a\alpha + b\beta) = a\phi(\alpha) + b\phi(\beta) \qquad (a, b \in F; \alpha, \beta \in V).$$

Examples

1. The function from R^3 to R

$$\phi: (x_1, x_2, x_3) \longmapsto x_1 \qquad ((x_1, x_2, x_3) \in R^3)$$

is a linear functional because its domain is a vector space over the field R, its codomain is R, and it is linear.

* See Example 1 on page K7, which we discussed in *Unit 1*.

Proof of linearity: if a, b are any scalars, and $\xi = (x_1, x_2, x_3)$ and $\eta = (y_1, y_2, y_3)$ are any vectors in R^3, we have

$$\phi(\xi) = x_1$$
$$\phi(\eta) = y_1$$
$$\phi(a\xi + b\eta) = \phi(ax_1 + by_1, ax_2 + by_2, ax_3 + by_3)$$
$$= ax_1 + by_1$$
$$= a\phi(\xi) + b\phi(\eta)$$

2. The function

$$\psi: (x_1, x_2, x_3) \longmapsto x_1 + 2x_2 + 3x_3 + c \qquad ((x_1, x_2, x_3) \in R^3)$$

where c is a real number, is a linear functional if and only if $c = 0$, since the image of the zero vector must be zero in order for ψ to be linear.

To summarize, a mapping whose domain is a real vector space has to satisfy two requirements to qualify as a linear functional:

(i) it must be a linear transformation;
(ii) its codomain must be R.

Exercises

1. Do Exercise 1 on page N131, ignoring the two sentences containing the symbol $\hat{A}$.

2. Which of the following mappings are linear functionals on P_3, the vector space consisting of all real polynomial functions of degree 2 or less?

   (a) $f \longmapsto f'$, the derived function

   (b) $f \longmapsto \int_0^1 f$

   (c) $f \longmapsto F$, where F is the primitive function of f defined by

   $$F: x \longmapsto \int_0^x f \qquad (x \in R)$$

   (d) $f \longmapsto f(2)$

   (e) $f \longmapsto f'(2)$

   (f) $f \longmapsto \int_0^1 f^2$

Solutions

1. (a), (c) and (d) are linear functionals.
   (b) is not, since, for example.

   $$\phi(2x_1, 0, 0) = 4x_1^2 \neq 2\phi(x_1, 0, 0).$$

   (e) is not, since, for example,

   $$\phi(0, 0, 0) \neq 0.$$

2. Only (b), (d) and (e) are linear functionals. The mappings (a) and (c) are not, because they map P_3 to P_2 and P_4 respectively, not to R. The mapping (f) maps P_3 to R, but it is not linear.

12.1.2   The Dual Space of V

In this sub-section we obtain the mathematical concept corresponding to the "greengrocer's space" discussed in the Introduction to this unit. If the original space ("customer's space") with typical element say $(a, b, c, \ldots)$ is a vector space V then each "price list", typically $[A, B, C, \ldots]$, gives rise to a linear functional on V

$$(a, b, c, \ldots) \longmapsto Aa + Bb + Cc \cdots$$

The set of all such linear functionals is called the dual space of V and denoted by $\hat{V}$ (usually pronounced "V hat" or "V cap"). The main results of this sub-section of the unit are that $\hat{V}$ is itself a vector space, and that if V has finite dimension n, then so does $\hat{V}$.

To make it a little easier to visualize the elements of $\hat{V}$ before embarking on the proofs of these statements, we consider the matrix representation of a linear functional ϕ. The general rule for matrix representations (see page N38) is that each column of the matrix contains the coordinates (with respect to the codomain basis) of the image of one of the domain basis vectors. If the domain has dimension n and codomain dimension m, then the matrix has m rows and n columns. Thus, in our case, if the domain V is n-dimensional, there are n columns in the matrix; the codomain is one-dimensional, and so the matrix has only one row. Thus any linear functional over an n-dimensional vector space V can be represented by a one-row matrix of the form

$$B = [b_1 \; b_2 \; \cdots \; b_n]. \tag{1}$$

This is the reason why we used square brackets to describe the price lists in our shopping example. You will recall from *Unit 2, Linear Transformations*, that $(x_1, \ldots, x_n)$ with *round* brackets is a space-saving way of writing

$$\begin{bmatrix} x_1 \\ \vdots \\ x_n \end{bmatrix}.$$

This is the representation for the elements of V itself. The images under the linear functional represented by B are then of the form

$$BX = b_1 x_1 + b_2 x_2 + \cdots + b_n x_n.$$

We studied this representation in *Unit 2* (see page N41).

It is fairly obvious from the one-row matrix representation (1) for linear functionals over V, that these functionals form a vector space and that its dimension is n. We now set about proving these statements.

Theorem 1

The set of all linear functionals on V forms a vector space. (You may remember that we have already proved this result in *Unit 2*, where we saw that the set of all linear transformations from one vector space to another forms a vector space. See page N30. But it is important enough to go over again.)

Proof

First of all, what do we mean by asserting that the linear functionals on V form a vector space? What operations would count as vector addition and scalar multiplication?

The answer is that linear functionals are functions, and we add them by means of the corresponding operations on the codomain. That is to say, if ϕ and ψ are linear functionals, then we define $\phi + \psi$ by:

$$(\phi + \psi)(\alpha) = \phi(\alpha) + \psi(\alpha) \qquad (\alpha \in V)$$

9

and similarly, we define $a\phi$ by:

$$(a\phi)(\alpha) = a\phi(\alpha) \qquad (\alpha \in V, a \in F)$$

The next stage in the proof is to check that $\phi + \psi$ and $a\phi$ are actually linear functionals. To this end, we let b, c be any scalars, and β, γ be any vectors in V, and check that:

$$(\phi + \psi)(b\beta + c\gamma) = b(\phi + \psi)(\beta) + c(\phi + \psi)(\gamma), \qquad (2)$$

$$(a\phi)(b\beta + c\gamma) = b(a\phi)(\beta) + c(a\phi)(\gamma). \qquad (3)$$

For Equation (2)

$$\begin{aligned}
(\phi + \psi)(b\beta + c\gamma) &= \phi(b\beta + c\gamma) + \psi(b\beta + c\gamma) \\
&= b\phi(\beta) + c\phi(\gamma) + b\psi(\beta) + c\psi(\gamma) \\
&= b(\phi(\beta) + \psi(\beta)) + c(\phi(\gamma) + \psi(\gamma)) \\
&= b(\phi + \psi)(\beta) + c(\phi + \psi)(\gamma)
\end{aligned}$$

For Equation (3)

$$\begin{aligned}
(a\phi)(b\beta + c\gamma) &= a(\phi(b\beta + c\gamma)) \\
&= a(b\phi(\beta) + c\phi(\gamma)) \\
&= ab\phi(\beta) + ac\phi(\gamma) \\
&= b(a\phi)(\beta) + c(a\phi)(\gamma).
\end{aligned}$$

It is a routine matter to check that the laws of associativity, distributivity, etc., hold for the above operations. If you feel that you need practice at some of them, then by all means work your way down the list of axioms on pages N7–8. Otherwise, don't bother.

Let us now set this new space in its context. First of all, we need a name and symbol for it.

Definition

The vector space of all linear functionals on V is called the *dual space* of V, and is denoted by $\hat{V}$.

We constructed $\hat{V}$ as a function space; that is we defined addition and scalar multiplication in terms of the corresponding operations in the codomain of the functions which are the elements of $\hat{V}$. This is not a new idea: besides spaces of polynomials, continuous functions, continuously differentiable functions, etc., we have seen *linear transformations from V to U* added and multiplied by scalars:

$$(\sigma + \tau)(\alpha) = \sigma(\alpha) + \tau(\alpha)$$

$$(a\sigma)(\alpha) = a(\sigma(\alpha)).$$

Here too, we could conveniently find the sum $\sigma + \tau$ by finding the sum of the matrices representing them. In fact, as we saw in *Unit 2*, the set of all linear transformations from V to U is itself a vector space, and $\hat{V}$ is merely a particular case of this, when U is just the field of scalars.

Before discussing Theorem 1 we saw that it is convenient to represent elements of $\hat{V}$ by one-row matrices; the number of rows in the matrix of a transformation is equal to the dimension of the codomain, which is in this case 1. We can use this matrix representation to find the dimension of $\hat{V}$. After all, to find the dimension of $\hat{V}$, we look for a basis of $\hat{V}$, and it is very strongly to be presumed that the required basis consists of elements having matrices

$$\begin{aligned}
&[1 \quad 0 \quad \ldots \quad 0], \\
&[0 \quad 1 \quad \ldots \quad 0], \\
&\quad \vdots \\
&[0 \quad 0 \quad \ldots \quad 1].
\end{aligned}$$

This gives a strong hint about the dimension of $\hat{V}$, which is the subject of the next theorem.

Theorem 2

If V is an n-dimensional vector space, then so is $\hat{V}$.

The following exercise is a preparation for the proof of Theorem 2.

Exercise

Let $\{\alpha_1, \alpha_2, \alpha_3\}$ be the standard basis of R^3 (i.e. in matrix form, $\alpha_1 = \begin{bmatrix} 1 \\ 0 \\ 0 \end{bmatrix}$,

$\alpha_2 = \begin{bmatrix} 0 \\ 1 \\ 0 \end{bmatrix}$, $\alpha_3 = \begin{bmatrix} 0 \\ 0 \\ 1 \end{bmatrix}$), and let ϕ_1, ϕ_2, ϕ_3 and the elements of $\widehat{R^3}$ with

matrices [1 0 0], [0 1 0], [0 0 1] respectively.

Find $\phi_i(\alpha_j)$ for each $i, j = 1, 2, 3$.

Solution

$\phi_i(\alpha_j)$ is the ith coordinate of α_j. Thus:

$$\phi_1(\alpha_1) = 1, \quad \phi_1(\alpha_2) = 0, \quad \phi_1(\alpha_3) = 0,$$
$$\phi_2(\alpha_1) = 0, \quad \phi_2(\alpha_2) = 1, \quad \phi_2(\alpha_3) = 0,$$
$$\phi_3(\alpha_1) = 0, \quad \phi_3(\alpha_2) = 0, \quad \phi_3(\alpha_3) = 1,$$

or, more concisely,

$$\phi_i(\alpha_j) = \begin{cases} 1 & \text{if } i = j \\ 0 & \text{if } i \neq j \end{cases}$$

We can write this even more concisely using the Kronecker delta, which we met in *Unit 1, Vector Spaces*, (see page N15):

$$\phi_i(\alpha_j) = \delta_{ij}$$

All that is necessary now, is to generalize from R^3 to the general case.

Proof of Theorem 2

Let $\{\alpha_1, \ldots, \alpha_n\}$ be a basis of V. From the result of the exercise above, it would appear that our strategy should be to find a set $\{\phi_1, \ldots, \phi_n\}$ of elements of $\hat{V}$, obeying

$$\phi_i(\alpha_j) = \delta_{ij} \qquad (i, j = 1, \ldots, n), \tag{4}$$

and prove that it is a basis. Such a set is to hand at once; for we saw in *Unit 2* (**Theorem 1.17**, page N34) that a linear transformation from V to U is uniquely defined by its effect on a basis of V. For each fixed i, Equation (4) defines the effect of ϕ_i on each of $\alpha_1, \alpha_2, \ldots, \alpha_n$:

$$\phi_i(\alpha_1) = \delta_{i1}, \phi_i(\alpha_2) = \delta_{i2}, \ldots, \phi_i(\alpha_n) = \delta_{in}.$$

Thus $\{\phi_1, \ldots, \phi_n\}$ is completely and uniquely specified by Equation (4) and all we have to do is to prove that:

(a) $\{\phi_1, \ldots, \phi_n\}$ is a linearly independent set;

(b) $\{\phi_1, \ldots, \phi_n\}$ spans $\hat{V}$.

We now set about proving each of these in turn.

Proof of (a)

To say that $\{\phi_1, \ldots, \phi_n\}$ is linearly independent is to say that no linear combination of the ϕ_i (except the trivial combination $0\phi_1 + 0\phi_2 + \cdots + 0\phi_n$) can be the zero functional. So we will take an arbitrary linear combination $a_1\phi_1 + \cdots + a_n\phi_n$, and show that if this *is* equal to the zero functional, then $a_1 = a_2 = \cdots = a_n = 0$.

Now if $a_1\phi_1 + \cdots + a_n\phi_n$ is the zero functional, then the image of every vector in V is zero under this functional. Consider α_1, for instance.

$$(a_1\phi_1 + \cdots + a_n\phi_n)(\alpha_1) = a_1\phi_1(\alpha_1) + a_2\phi_2(\alpha_1) + \cdots + a_n\phi_n(\alpha_1).$$

But, by Equation (4),

$$\phi_2(\alpha_1) = \phi_3(\alpha_1) = \cdots = \phi_n(\alpha_1) = 0,$$

and

$$\phi_1(\alpha_1) = 1.$$

Thus

$$(a_1\phi_1 + \cdots + a_n\phi_n)(\alpha_1) = a_1.$$

By an exactly similar argument,

$$(a_1\phi_1 + \cdots + a_n\phi_n)(\alpha_2) = a_2,$$
$$\vdots$$
$$(a_1\phi_1 + \cdots + a_n\phi_n)(\alpha_n) = a_n.$$

So, if we assume that the image of *every* vector in V is zero, then it must be the case that $a_1 = a_2 = \cdots = a_n = 0$. And this is exactly what we require in order to assert that $\{\phi_1, \ldots, \phi_n\}$ is linearly independent.

Proof of (b)

To say that $\{\phi_1, \ldots, \phi_n\}$ spans $\hat{V}$ is to say that, if ψ is *any* element of $\hat{V}$, then ψ is a linear combination of $\phi_1, \ldots, \phi_n$.

Now ψ is defined by its action on the basis $\{\alpha_1, \ldots, \alpha_n\}$ of V. If

$$\psi(\alpha_1) = a_1$$
$$\psi(\alpha_2) = a_2$$
$$\vdots$$
$$\psi(\alpha_n) = a_n,$$

then $[a_1 \cdots a_n]$ is the matrix representing ψ with respect to the basis $\{\alpha_1, \ldots, \alpha_n\}$ of V. We may take the matrix representatives of $\phi_1, \ldots, \phi_n$ as $[1 \quad 0 \cdots 0], \ldots, [0 \cdots 0 \quad 1]$; then, since

$$[a_1 \cdots a_n] = a_1[1 \quad 0 \cdots 0] + \cdots + a_n[0 \cdots 0 \quad 1],$$

it is presumably the case that

$$\psi = a_1\phi_1 + \cdots + a_n\phi_n. \tag{5}$$

Since a linear transformation is completely described by its effect on a basis, all we have to do is to ensure that the two sides of Formula (5) have the same effect on every element of a basis of V:

$$\psi(\alpha_1) = (a_1\phi_1 + \cdots + a_n\phi_n)(\alpha_1)$$
$$\psi(\alpha_2) = (a_1\phi_1 + \cdots + a_n\phi_n)(\alpha_2)$$
$$\vdots$$
$$\psi(\alpha_n) = (a_1\phi_1 + \cdots + a_n\phi_n)(\alpha_n)$$

This is easy; for any $j = 1, \ldots, n$, we have

$$(a_1\phi_1 + \cdots + a_n\phi_n)(\alpha_j) = a_1\phi_1(\alpha_j) + \cdots + a_j\phi_j(\alpha_j) + \cdots + a_n\phi_n(\alpha_j)$$
$$= a_j \qquad \text{(by Equation (4))}$$
$$= \psi(\alpha_j) \qquad \text{(by the definition of } \psi).$$

So we have proved that $\{\phi_1, \ldots, \phi_n\}$ spans $\hat{V}$.

Thus $\{\phi_1, \ldots, \phi_n\}$ is a basis of $\hat{V}$, which is therefore n-dimensional.

Exercise

If V is 3-dimensional and $\{\alpha_1, \alpha_2, \alpha_3\}$ is any basis for it, calculate $\phi(\alpha)$, where $\alpha = \alpha_1 + 2\alpha_2 - \sqrt{3}\alpha_3$, and $\phi = 4\phi_1 - 5\phi_2 + \sqrt{3}\phi_3$, with ϕ_1, ϕ_2, ϕ_3 defined as in Equation (4).

Solution

$$\phi_1(\alpha) = \phi_1(\alpha_1 + 2\alpha_2 - \sqrt{3}\alpha_3) = 1$$
(first coordinate of α)

$$\phi_2(\alpha) = \phi_2(\alpha_1 + 2\alpha_2 - \sqrt{3}\alpha_3) = 2$$
(second coordinate of α)

$$\phi_3(\alpha) = \phi_3(\alpha_1 + 2\alpha_2 - \sqrt{3}\alpha_3) = -\sqrt{3}.$$
(third coordinate of α)

Thus

$$\phi(\alpha) = 4\phi_1(\alpha) - 5\phi_2(\alpha) + \sqrt{3}\phi_3(\alpha)$$
$$= (4 \times 1) + (-5 \times 2) + (\sqrt{3} \times -\sqrt{3})$$
$$= 4 - 10 - 3 = -9.$$

12.1.3   The Dual Basis

We now have two distinct ways of representing a linear functional on V by numbers. On the one hand, we can think of it as a linear transformation from V to F and represent it (with respect to some given basis $\{\alpha_1, \ldots, \alpha_n\}$ in V) by a one-row matrix of the form

$$[b_1 \; b_2 \ldots b_n].$$

On the other hand, we can regard it as an element of the vector space $\hat{V}$, and represent it by the n-tuple of coordinates with respect to a basis $\{\phi_1, \ldots, \phi_n\}$ in $\hat{V}$; if the linear functional is

$$b_1\phi_1 + \cdots + b_n\phi_n,$$

this n-tuple is

$$(b_1, \ldots, b_n).$$

Obviously it would be convenient if the numbers $b_1, \ldots, b_n$ in the two representations were the same; and we can achieve precisely this by taking $\{\phi_1, \ldots, \phi_n\}$ to be the basis defined in the preceding sub-section, by means of the formula $\phi_i(\alpha_j) = \delta_{ij}$ (see Equation (4), page C11).

Because of this useful property we give the basis $\{\phi_1, \ldots, \phi_n\}$ in $\hat{V}$ a special name.

Definition

If $\{\alpha_1, \ldots, \alpha_n\}$ is a basis of V, then the basis $\{\phi_1, \ldots, \phi_n\}$ of $\hat{V}$ defined by

$$\phi_i(\alpha_j) = \delta_{ij} \qquad (i, j = 1, \ldots, n)$$

is called the *dual basis* of $\hat{V}$ (i.e. the basis of $\hat{V}$ dual to $\{\alpha_1, \ldots, \alpha_n\}$).

If $\{\alpha_1, \ldots, \alpha_n\}$ is denoted by the symbol A, then we denote the dual basis by $\hat{A}$.

Although the basis A has a "dual", it does not follow that the individual vectors comprising it have individual duals. There is a natural one-one correspondence between *bases* in V and *bases* in $\hat{V}$, but not between *vectors* in V and *vectors* in $\hat{V}$. Perhaps the best way to illustrate this is to take a basis $\{\alpha_1, \alpha_2\}$ of R^2, with the dual basis $\{\phi_1, \phi_2\}$ of $\hat{V}$, then change *just one* of the basis elements of V. We find that *both* elements change in the dual basis (see the following example), which shows that this particular form of "duality" is a property of the basis as a whole, rather than individual vectors.

Example

Let $A = \{(1, 0), (0, 1)\}$, $\hat{A} = \{[1 \ 0], [0 \ 1]\}$ be the standard bases of R^2, $\widehat{R^2}$. Consider a new basis

$$A' = \{(-1, 2), (0, 1)\}$$

for R^2, in which the first basis element is different from the first basis element of A, but the second basis element is the same as the second basis element of A. What is the dual basis $\widehat{A'}$? We can determine this as follows.

Let

$$\widehat{A'} = \{\phi_1, \phi_2\} = \{[a \ b], [c \ d]\}.$$

Then

$$\phi_1'((-1, 2)) = 1, \qquad \phi_1'((0, 1)) = 0$$
$$\phi_2'((-1, 2)) = 0, \qquad \phi_2'((0, 1)) = 1$$

i.e.

$$-a + 2b = 1, \qquad b = 0$$
$$-c + 2d = 0, \qquad d = 1$$

so that

$$\phi_1' = [-1 \ 0], \phi_2' = [2 \ 1],$$

and *both* elements of the dual basis are different from the corresponding elements of the original dual basis. (It may interest you to notice, however, that ϕ_1 and ϕ_1' span the same subspace of $\hat{V}$. This is related to the fact that the *second* element of A is the same as the second element of A'.)

Example

What happens if we simply take for A' the negatives of the elements of A, i.e. if $A' = \{-\alpha_1, -\alpha_2, \ldots, -\alpha_n\}$? We would intuitively expect $\widehat{A'}$ to be just the negatives of the elements of $\hat{A}$ in this case, and this expectation is justified. We begin with the definitions of $\hat{A}$ and $\widehat{A'}$:

$$\phi_i(\alpha_j) = \delta_{ij} \tag{1}$$
$$\phi_i'(\alpha_j') = \delta_{ij} \tag{2}$$

Equation (2) implies

$$\phi_i'(-\alpha_j) = \delta_{ij}$$

so that

$$\phi_i'(\alpha_j) = -\delta_{ij}$$
$$= -\phi_i(\alpha_j), \text{ by Equation (1).}$$

As this is true for all i, j, it follows that

$$\phi_i' = -\phi_i \qquad (i = 1, \ldots, n).$$

Exercises

1. Let $\hat{A} = \{\phi_1, \ldots, \phi_n\}$ be the basis of $\hat{V}$ dual to the basis $A = \{\alpha_1, \ldots, \alpha_n\}$ of V.

    What are the bases dual to:

    (i) $\{2\alpha_1, 2\alpha_2, \ldots, 2\alpha_n\}$,
    (ii) $\{a_1\alpha_1, a_2\alpha_2, \ldots, a_n\alpha_n\}$

    where $a_1, \ldots, a_n$ are scalars, none of them being equal to zero?

2. Let V be a 2-dimensional vector space, with basis $A = \{\alpha_1, \alpha_2\}$.

Let the dual basis $\hat{A}$ of $\hat{V}$ be $\{\phi_1, \phi_2\}$.

(i)   Let $A' = \{\alpha_1 + 2\alpha_2, 3\alpha_1 + 4\alpha_2\}$. Find $\widehat{A'}$.

(ii) Now let $A' = \{a_1\alpha_1 + a_2\alpha_2, a_3\alpha_1 + a_4\alpha_2\}$.

Write out equations to determine
$$\widehat{A'} = \{b_1\phi_1 + b_2\phi_2, b_3\phi_1 + b_4\phi_2\}.$$

(iii) Write out the last equations as a matrix equation.

(iv) Take a guess at a matrix equation for finding a dual basis in an n-dimensional dual space.

3. Exercise 5, page N132.

Solutions

1. (i) $\phi_i'(\alpha_j') = \delta_{ij}$

that is
$$\phi_i'(2\alpha_j) = \delta_{ij}$$
$$2\phi_i'(\alpha_j) = \delta_{ij}$$
$$\phi_i'(\alpha_j) = \tfrac{1}{2}\delta_{ij}$$
$$= \tfrac{1}{2}(\phi_i(\alpha_j)) \text{ for all relevant } i, j.$$

Thus,
$$\phi_i' = \tfrac{1}{2}\phi_i \qquad (i = 1, \ldots, n),$$
and
$$\widehat{A'} = \tfrac{1}{2}\hat{A}.$$

(ii) $\phi_i'(\alpha_j') = \delta_{ij}$

that is
$$\phi_i'(a_j\alpha_j) = \delta_{ij}$$
$$a_j\phi_i'(\alpha_j) = \delta_{ij}$$
$$\phi_i'(\alpha_j) = \frac{1}{a_j}\delta_{ij} \qquad (\text{as } a_j \neq 0).$$

The only time δ_{ij} is not zero is when $i = j$, and so
$$\frac{1}{a_j}\delta_{ij} = \frac{1}{a_i}\delta_{ij}$$
$$= \frac{1}{a_i}(\phi_i(\alpha_j)).$$

Thus for each fixed i,
$$\phi_i'(\alpha_j) = \frac{1}{a_i}(\phi_i(\alpha_j))$$

as j varies from 1 to n.

Thus
$$\phi_i' = \frac{1}{a_i}\phi_i \qquad (i = 1, \ldots, n).$$

2. (i)   Let $A' = \{\phi_1', \phi_2'\} = \{a\phi_1 + b\phi_2, c\phi_1 + d\phi_2\}$.

We have the equations
$$\left.\begin{array}{l} \phi_1'(\alpha_1') = (a\phi_1 + b\phi_2)(\alpha_1 + 2\alpha_2) = 1 \\ \phi_1'(\alpha_2') = (a\phi_1 + b\phi_2)(3\alpha_1 + 4\alpha_2) = 0, \\ \phi_2'(\alpha_1') = (c\phi_1 + d\phi_2)(\alpha_1 + 2\alpha_2) = 0, \\ \phi_2'(\alpha_2') = (c\phi_1 + d\phi_2)(3\alpha_1 + 4\alpha_2) = 1 \end{array}\right\} \qquad (3)$$

That is

$$a + 2b = 1, \qquad 3a + 4b = 0$$
$$c + 2d = 0, \qquad 3c + 4d = 1 \tag{4}$$

Solving these equations gives

$$a = -2, \quad b = \tfrac{3}{2}, \quad c = 1, \quad d = -\tfrac{1}{2}$$

Thus

$$\phi_1' = -2\phi_1 + \tfrac{3}{2}\phi_2,$$
$$\phi_2' = \phi_1 - \tfrac{1}{2}\phi_2$$

and so

$$\widehat{A'} = \{-2\phi_1 + \tfrac{3}{2}\phi_2, \ \phi_1 - \tfrac{1}{2}\phi_2\}$$

(ii)   In this case

$$\phi_1'(\alpha_1') = (b_1\phi_1 + b_2\phi_2)(a_1\alpha_1 + a_2\alpha_2) = 1$$
$$\phi_1'(\alpha_2') = (b_1\phi_1 + b_2\phi_2)(a_3\alpha_1 + a_4\alpha_2) = 0$$
$$\phi_2'(\alpha_1') = (b_3\phi_1 + b_4\phi_2)(a_1\alpha_1 + a_2\alpha_2) = 0$$
$$\phi_2'(\alpha_2') = (b_3\phi_1 + b_4\phi_2)(a_3\alpha_1 + a_4\alpha_2) = 1$$

Thus

$$b_1a_1 + b_2a_2 = 1, \qquad b_1a_3 + b_2a_4 = 0,$$
$$b_3a_1 + b_4a_2 = 0, \qquad b_3a_3 + b_4a_4 = 1.$$

(iii) $$\begin{bmatrix} b_1 & b_2 \\ b_3 & b_4 \end{bmatrix} \begin{bmatrix} a_1 & a_3 \\ a_2 & a_4 \end{bmatrix} = \begin{bmatrix} 1 & 0 \\ 0 & 1 \end{bmatrix} = I.$$

(If in (ii) you wrote the equations out as $a_1b_1 + a_2b_2 = 1$, etc., then you would get the matrix equation

$$\begin{bmatrix} a_1 & a_2 \\ a_3 & a_4 \end{bmatrix} \begin{bmatrix} b_1 & b_3 \\ b_2 & b_4 \end{bmatrix} = I$$

from which the equation

$$\begin{bmatrix} b_1 & b_2 \\ b_3 & b_4 \end{bmatrix} \begin{bmatrix} a_1 & a_3 \\ a_2 & a_4 \end{bmatrix} = I$$

can be obtained simply by taking the transpose of each side: remember that $(AB)^T = B^T A^T$.)

(iv)   In (iii), we see that

$$RP = I$$

where the columns of P are the coordinates of the new basis of V with respect to the original basis and the rows of R are the coordinates of the new dual basis of $\widehat{V}$ with respect to the original dual basis. It is therefore a reasonable guess that this equation holds in n dimensions also. Since this means that $R = P^{-1}$, we have a rule:

To find the coordinates of the new dual basis of $\widehat{V}$ with respect to the old dual basis, write out the matrix whose columns consist of the coordinates of the new basis of V with respect to the old basis. Invert it, and read off the rows of the inverse matrix.

This can be put in terms of matrices of transition. You saw in *Unit 3, Hermite Normal Form*, (page N50) that the matrix whose columns are coordinates of a new basis with respect to an old basis, is called the *matrix of transition*. Thus, in this case, P is the matrix of transition from the old basis A of V to the new basis A'.

However, the matrix R is not the matrix of transition from the old dual basis $\widehat{A}$ to the new dual basis $\widehat{A'}$, since it is the *rows* of R, and not the columns, that express the new dual basis in terms of the old. This is quite easy to rectify, though; for if we let Q be the *transpose* of R, then the columns of Q are the rows of R, and so Q *is* the matrix of transition from $\hat{A}$ to $\hat{A'}$.

Thus the relation between the matrices of transition P, Q in V and $\hat{V}$ respectively, is:

$$Q = R^T$$

i.e.

$$Q = (P^{-1})^T.$$

3.   (See N's answer on page N332.)

The problem asks us to show that when α is expressed as a linear combination of the basis vectors $\{\alpha_1, \ldots, \alpha_n\}$, the coefficient of α_i is $\phi_i(\alpha)$; in other words, that if

$$\alpha = a_1\alpha_1 + \cdots + a_n\alpha_n, \tag{5}$$

then

$$a_i = \phi_i(\alpha) \qquad (i = 1, \ldots, n).$$

What do we know about ϕ_i? It is defined here as an element of the dual basis, i.e.

$$\phi_i(\alpha_j) = \delta_{ij}. \tag{6}$$

The number we want is $\phi_i(\alpha)$. Using the linearity of ϕ_i, we can get this from Equations (5) and (6):

$$\begin{aligned}
\phi_i(\alpha) &= a_1\phi_i(\alpha_1) + \cdots + a_i\phi_i(\alpha_i) + \cdots + a_n\phi_i(\alpha_n) \\
&= a_1 \times 0 + \cdots + a_i \times 1 + \cdots + a_n \times 0 \\
&= a_i.
\end{aligned}$$

Since this holds for $i = 1, 2, \ldots, n$, Equation (5) for α can now be written

$$\alpha = \phi_1(\alpha)\alpha_1 + \cdots + \phi_n(\alpha)\alpha_n,$$

which is the result we want.

Notice how the solution uses the fact that $\{\alpha_1, \ldots, \alpha_n\}$ is a basis: the fact that it spans V justifies writing α in the form of Equation (5), and the fact that it is linearly independent makes the numbers a_i appearing in Equation (5) unique, and so justifies taking Equation (5) as our definition of these numbers.

The rule given in the solution to Exercise (2) is confirmed in the following theorem. We have left blanks in the proof for you to fill in. You should not have too much difficulty; if you do, read the solutions to the exercises in this section again, carefully. Remember also that, if p_{ij} is a typical matrix entry of a matrix P, then the *first* suffix i refers to the *row* which p_{ij} is in, while the *second* suffix j refers to the *column*.

Theorem 3

Let V be a vector space with basis $A = \{\alpha_1, \ldots, \alpha_n\}$, and let $\hat{A} = \{\phi_1, \ldots, \phi_n\}$ be the dual basis in $\hat{V}$. If A' is a new basis of V, whose coordinates with respect to A are the columns of an $n \times n$ matrix P, then the coordinates of $\widehat{A'}$ with respect to $\hat{A}$ are the rows of an $n \times n$ matrix R, where

$$RP = I$$

i.e.

$$R = P^{-1}$$

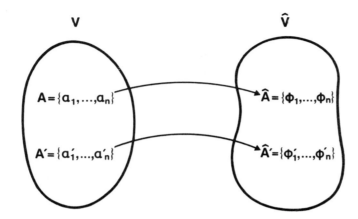

In other words, if P is the matrix of transition from A to A' and Q is the matrix of transition from $\hat{A}$ to $\hat{A}'$, then since Q is thus equal to R^T, we obtain the equation

$$Q = (P^{-1})^T.$$

Proof

If the components of $A' = \{\alpha'_1, \ldots, \alpha'_n\}$ with respect to A are the columns of $P = [p_{ij}]$, then since $p_{1j}, \ldots, p_{nj}$ are the elements of the jth column of the matrix P,

$$\alpha'_j = \sum_{k=1}^{n} \underline{\hspace{4cm}} \text{(i)}$$

If the components of $\widehat{A'} = \{\phi'_1, \ldots, \phi'_n\}$ with respect to $\hat{A}$ are the rows of $R = [r_{ij}]$, then, since $r_{i1}, \ldots, r_{in}$ are the elements of the ith row of the matrix R,

$$\phi'_i = \sum_{l=1}^{n} \underline{\hspace{4cm}} \text{(ii)}$$

Thus

$$\phi'_i(\alpha'_j) = \sum_{k=1}^{n} \sum_{l=1}^{n} \underline{\hspace{3cm}} \phi_l(\alpha_k) \quad \text{(iii)}$$

But since $\phi_l(\alpha_k) = \delta_{lk}$ we only need to sum over l, and we can set $k = l$.

Thus

$$\phi'_i(\alpha'_j) = \sum_{l=1}^{n} \underline{\hspace{4cm}} \text{(iv)}$$

But the left-hand side of (iv) is the (ij)th entry of the matrix$\underline{\hspace{2cm}}$ (v) and the right-hand side is the (ij)th entry of the matrix$\underline{\hspace{2cm}}$ (vi)

Thus $RP = I$, as required, and since the matrix of transition Q is R^T, we get the equation

$$Q = (P^{-1})^T$$

18

The blanks should be filled in as follows:

(i) $\quad \alpha'_j = \sum_{k=1}^{n} p_{kj}\alpha_k$ $\qquad$ (ii) $\quad \phi'_i = \sum_{l=1}^{n} r_{il}\phi_l$

(iii) $\quad \phi'(\alpha'_j) = \sum_{k=1}^{n}\sum_{l=1}^{n} r_{il}p_{kj}\phi_l(\alpha_k)$ $\qquad$ (iv) $\quad \phi'_i(\alpha'_j) = \sum_{l=1}^{n} r_{il}p_{lj}$ $\qquad$ (v) $\quad I$

(vi) $\quad RP$

Exercise

Exercise 2, page N131. (If you have forgotten how to calculate the inverse of a matrix, see page N61.)

Solution

(a) Writing the components of $\{(1, 0, 0), (0, 1, 0), (0, 0, 1)\}$ as the columns of a matrix P simply makes P into the unit matrix I, which is its own inverse. Reading off the rows of I:

$$\hat{A} = \{[1 \quad 0 \quad 0], \quad [0 \quad 1 \quad 0], \quad [0 \quad 0 \quad 1]\}.$$

(b)
$$P = \begin{bmatrix} 1 & 1 & 1 \\ 0 & 1 & 1 \\ 0 & 0 & 1 \end{bmatrix}$$

We can invert P by finding the Hermite normal form of

$$\begin{bmatrix} 1 & 1 & 1 & 1 & 0 & 0 \\ 0 & 1 & 1 & 0 & 1 & 0 \\ 0 & 0 & 1 & 0 & 0 & 1 \end{bmatrix},$$

which is

$$\begin{bmatrix} 1 & 0 & 0 & 1 & -1 & 0 \\ 0 & 1 & 0 & 0 & 1 & -1 \\ 0 & 0 & 1 & 0 & 0 & 1 \end{bmatrix}$$

Thus:

$$P^{-1} = \begin{bmatrix} 1 & -1 & 0 \\ 0 & 1 & -1 \\ 0 & 0 & 1 \end{bmatrix},$$

and so

$$\hat{A} = \{[1 \quad -1 \quad 0], \quad [0 \quad 1 \quad -1], \quad [0 \quad 0 \quad 1]\}.$$

(c)
$$P = \begin{bmatrix} 1 & -1 & 0 \\ 0 & 1 & 1 \\ -1 & 0 & 1 \end{bmatrix}$$

The Hermite normal form of

$$\begin{bmatrix} 1 & -1 & 0 & 1 & 0 & 0 \\ 0 & 1 & 1 & 0 & 1 & 0 \\ -1 & 0 & 1 & 0 & 0 & 1 \end{bmatrix}$$

is

$$\begin{bmatrix} 1 & 0 & 0 & \frac{1}{2} & \frac{1}{2} & -\frac{1}{2} \\ 0 & 1 & 0 & -\frac{1}{2} & \frac{1}{2} & -\frac{1}{2} \\ 0 & 0 & 1 & \frac{1}{2} & \frac{1}{2} & \frac{1}{2} \end{bmatrix}$$

Thus

$$\hat{A} = \{[\tfrac{1}{2} \quad \tfrac{1}{2} \quad -\!-\tfrac{1}{2}], \quad [-\tfrac{1}{2} \quad \tfrac{1}{2} \quad -\tfrac{1}{2}], \quad [\tfrac{1}{2} \quad \tfrac{1}{2} \quad \tfrac{1}{2}]\}.$$

19

12.1.4 Using the Dual Basis—an Example (Optional)

The "dual basis" concept is important in the study of crystals, because of the regularity of structure of a crystal.

The simplest sort of crystal is one whose basic structure is that of parallele-pipeds*, as in the following diagram.

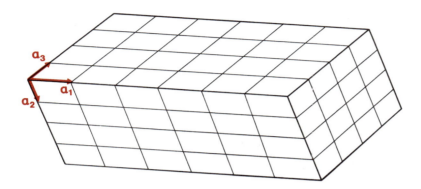

To make the thing easier to visualize, we will consider a "2-dimensional crystal", i.e. a splitting up of the 2-dimensional x, y plane into parallelo-gram-shaped "crystal cells".

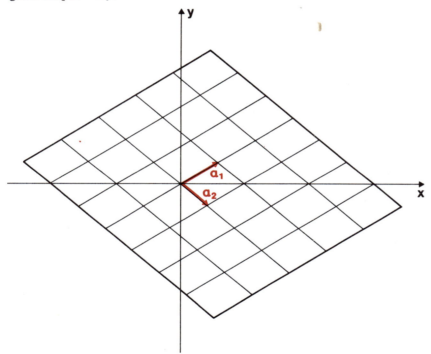

A crystallographer is interested in functions that are periodic in the crystal; that is, functions whose values depend only on the position within a given "cell" of the crystal, and not on which "cell" is being considered. It is clearly sensible to consider such functions, for owing to the regularity of structure of the crystals, one would expect such a quantity as electric potential, or mechanical stress, to vary within a cell but to be independent of which cell one was in. (Strictly speaking, this would not apply to cells which are near the surface of the crystal, where strange things might be happening, but for a large crystal such an assumption would certainly seem reasonable for cells deep inside the crystal.)

* A parallelepiped is a polyhedron figure whose faces are all parallelograms.

Mathematically, such a function is characterized as follows:

$$f(\alpha) = f(\alpha + n_1\alpha_1 + n_2\alpha_2) \qquad (n_1, n_2 \in Z)$$

in the 2-dimensional case, or

$$f(\alpha) = f(\alpha + n_1\alpha_1 + n_2\alpha_2 + n_3\alpha_3) \qquad (n_1, n_2, n_3 \in Z)$$

in the 3-dimensional case.

That is, the image under the function is unchanged if the element in the domain is translated by a whole number of "steps", each of which translates a point within one cell to a corresponding point in an adjacent cell. The obvious functions to choose in order to try to obtain periodicity, are sine and cosine functions, as these are periodic:

$$\sin x = \sin (x + n_1 \times 2\pi) \qquad (n_1 \in Z)$$

(Imagine a "one-dimensional crystal" whose "cell" is of length 2π.)

In the 2- and 3-dimensional cases, sines and cosines of vector quantities are not defined, so we must convert the vector quantities α_1, α_2, α_3, etc., into scalars. What could be more natural than to do this by applying linear functionals to them?

So we want to find linear functionals ϕ_i such that the functions

$$f_i: \alpha \longmapsto \sin (\phi_i(\alpha))$$

are periodic with respect to the required crystal cells. It turns out that the appropriate ϕ_i can be obtained from the dual basis to the basis $\{\alpha_i\}$.

The functions

$$\alpha \longmapsto \sin (2\pi k_i\phi_i(\alpha))$$
$$\alpha \longmapsto \cos (2\pi k_i\phi_i(\alpha)), \qquad (k_i \in Z)$$

are periodic with respect to the crystal cells, because, for example,

$$\begin{aligned}
\sin (2\pi k_i\phi_i(\alpha + n_j\alpha_j)) &= \sin 2\pi k_i[\phi_i(\alpha) + n_j\phi_i(\alpha_j)] \\
&= \sin 2\pi k_i[\phi_i(\alpha) + n_j\delta_{ij}] \\
&= \sin (2\pi k_i\phi_i(\alpha)).
\end{aligned}$$

Further, they can be used to form a basis for the set of functions in which the crystallographer is interested.

12.1.5 Summary of Section 12.1

In this section we defined the terms

linear functional	(page C5)	★ ★ ★
dual space	(page C10)	★ ★ ★
dual basis	(page C13)	★ ★ ★

Theorems

1. (page C9)
The set of all linear functionals on V forms a vector space.   ★ ★ ★

2. (page C11)
If V is n-dimensional, so is $\hat{V}$.   ★ ★ ★

3. (page C18)
Let V be a vector space with basis A and let $\hat{A}$ be the dual basis in $\hat{V}$. If A' is a new basis of V and the matrix of transition from A to A' is P, then the coordinates of $\hat{A'}$ with respect to $\hat{A}$ are the columns of Q, the matrix of transition from $\hat{A}$ to $\hat{A'}$, and $Q = (P^{-1})^T$.   ★

Technique

Given a basis A of a vector space V, determine the corresponding dual basis $\hat{A}$ in the dual vector space $\hat{V}$.   ★ ★ ★

Notation

$[a\ b\ c\ \cdots]$	(page C9)
$\hat{V}$	(page C9)
$\hat{A}$	(page C13)

Vectors in V are represented by one-column matrices. Vectors in $\hat{V}$ are represented by one-row matrices.

READ Section IV-1 of N, *starting on page* N129, *and Section IV-3, starting on page* N134, *as far as line 19, page* N135, *and then from line-10, page* N137 *to the end of the section.*

12.2 DUALITY

12.2.1 Exchanging Function and Domain

In the example considered in the Introduction to this unit, there was a symmetrical relationship between the "customer's space" and the "green-grocer's space". The customer's linear functionals (price lists) correspond to the greengrocer's vectors, and the customer's vectors correspond to the greengrocer's linear functionals.

When we generalized this idea to vector spaces, we did so in a rather unsymmetrical way: we showed that the linear functionals in any space V could be regarded as vectors in its dual space $\hat{V}$, but we did not show that the vectors in V could be regarded as linear functionals on $\hat{V}$.

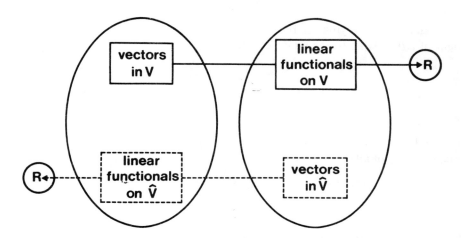

In the present sub-section, we study the linear functionals on $\hat{V}$ and see whether they do correspond in a natural way to vectors in V.

In the case of finite-dimensional spaces, the matrix representation makes it very plausible that such a correspondence does exist. We have seen that every element of $\hat{V}$ (that is, every linear functional on V) can be represented as a one-row matrix, say $[b_1 \ldots b_n]$, where n is the dimension of V and $\hat{V}$. A linear functional on $\hat{V}$ is therefore equivalent to a function from the set of all ordered n-tuples of the form $[b_1 \ldots b_n]$ to the field of scalars F. Such a linear functional will be of the form

$$[b_1 \ldots b_n] \longmapsto a_1 b_1 + \cdots + a_n b_n \quad ([b_1 \ldots b_n] \in \hat{V})$$

where $a_1, \ldots, a_n$ are scalars, and it can therefore be written in matrix notation as

$$[b_1 \ldots b_n] \longmapsto [b_1 \ldots b_n]\begin{bmatrix} a_1 \\ \vdots \\ a_n \end{bmatrix} \tag{1}$$

The scalars $a_1, \ldots, a_n$ characterize the mapping, and in this way every linear functional on $\hat{V}$ can be represented by a one-column matrix $\begin{bmatrix} a_1 \\ \vdots \\ a_n \end{bmatrix}$

We have seen already, however, that the vectors in V are represented by one-column matrices. Thus the correspondence we are looking for can be set up via the one-column matrix representation.

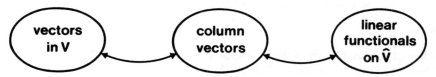

The above argument, however, is open to the objection that it makes use of a particular matrix representation; since matrix representations depend on the basis used, it is not clear whether the correspondence we have set up between the vectors in V and the linear transformations on $\hat{V}$ depends on the basis or not. In fact, this correspondence does *not* depend on the basis, and that is the reason for its importance. But to prove this independence we must find a basis-independent way of describing the correspondence. Just as we have done several times before in this unit, we can get a strong clue to how this correspondence comes about by looking at the way the matrix representation works out. What we have been saying essentially is that in the expression

$$[b_1 \ldots b_n]\begin{bmatrix} a_1 \\ \vdots \\ a_n \end{bmatrix}$$

we can either regard the as as fixed and the bs varying, or the bs as fixed and as varying. It can be thought of *either* as an image under a function specified by

$$\begin{bmatrix} a_1 \\ \vdots \\ a_n \end{bmatrix}$$

with domain the set of all $[b_1 \ldots b_n]$, *or* as an image under a function specified by $[b_1 \ldots b_n]$, with domain the set of all

$$\begin{bmatrix} a_1 \\ \vdots \\ a_n \end{bmatrix}$$

It's purely and simply a question of swapping the roles of function space and domain. Whether we can carry out this swap in a mathematically satisfactory way, depends solely on our ability to juggle with the concepts of "function" and "domain", and not at all on the nature of the *particular* function space and domain being considered.

Example

John, Jack and Jill get the following percentages in their end-of-term school exams, for English, Maths and Science.

	John	Jack	Jill
English	62	50	60
Maths	78	40	60
Science	61	49	60

This table can be read in two ways. The headmaster might be interested in how John, Jack and Jill are doing in their various subjects. For example, he would regard "John" as a function whose domain is the set of subjects:

John : English $\longmapsto$ 62, etc.

An educational psychologist, however, might look at the above figure rather differently. He might wish to compare the teaching success of the English, Maths and Science teachers. To do this, he would perhaps regard "Maths", for example, as a function whose domain is the set of pupils:

Maths : John $\longmapsto$ 78, etc.

Our object is to find a concise mathematical description of this "swapping" process. If we treat the two sets (English, Maths, Science) and (John, Jack,

Jill) on a par, then the above table is really describing a function on the Cartesian product:

$$F: (\text{English, Maths, Science}) \times (\text{John, Jack, Jill}) \longrightarrow R$$

Thus,

$$F((\text{English, Jack})) = 50$$
$$F((\text{Science, John})) = 61$$

etc.

Essentially, we have a similar situation to the one we had in *Unit M100 19, Relations*, where we saw that a function $f: A \longrightarrow B$ had an alternative mathematical description as a *relation* on the set $A \times B$. Here, too, we have an alternative mathematical description of a situation: if S is a set of functions with domain T and codomain R, then we can alternatively describe the situation as a function $F: S \times T \longrightarrow R$, where

$$F(f,x) = f(x) \qquad (f \in S, x \in T)$$

or again as a set $\tilde{T}$ of functions with domain S and codomain R. (You can pronounce $\tilde{T}$, "T—tilde" or "T—twiddle".)

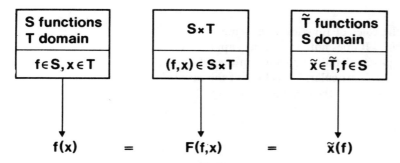

We write $\tilde{T}$ instead of T if we are thinking of T as defining a set of functions, and $\tilde{x}$ instead of x ($x \in T$) because an element of T, the domain of S, is not *exactly* the same thing as a function with domain S. There is, rather, a *natural correspondence* between x and $\tilde{x}$, given by

$$\tilde{x}(f) = f(x) \qquad (x \in T, f \in S) \tag{2}$$

Equation (2) is a most important equation, as it expresses this particular aspect of duality: "function space" and "domain" are dual concepts, and can exchange roles by means of Equation (2). In terms of our example, we have the following situation. If (John, Jack, Jill) is the function space, and (English, Maths, Science) the domain, then one has functions:

$$\text{John(English)} = 62, \text{John(Maths)} = 78, \text{etc.}$$
$$\text{Jack(English)} = 50, \text{etc.}$$

We know that English, Maths and Science can be regarded as functions, and we put $\sim$ above them to distinguish between their role as functions and their role as elements of a domain:

$$\tilde{\text{English}}(\text{John}) = 62, \tilde{\text{English}}(\text{Jack}) = 50, \text{etc.}$$

Exercise

Let T be the set of all Open University Students. Define a set S of functions with domain T and codomain R, corresponding to the set of counties in Britain:

$$S = (\text{Yorkshire, Lancashire, Hertfordshire}, \ldots)$$

where

$$\tilde{\text{Yorkshire}}(x) = 1 \text{ if } x \text{ lives in Yorkshire}$$

and

Yorkshire(x) = 0 if x does not live in Yorkshire, etc.

If Montague Z. Delacourt-Ponsonby lives in Lancashire, describe the function

(Montague Z. Delacourt-Ponsonby)˜.

(The $\sim$ outside the parentheses means the same as one above the element.)

Solution

The domain of the function is the set of all counties, and the images are given by

(Montague Z. Delacourt-Ponsonby)˜(Lancashire) = 1,

(Montague Z. Delacourt-Ponsonby)˜(t) = 0

($t \in S$, $t \neq$ Lancashire).

12.2.2   Duality and Linear Functionals

The above account of exchanging the roles of function and domain may well generate the comment: " so what?" It does not, as it stands, appear to lead very far. However, when we impose a definite structure on the sets S and T, we get some interesting results. In particular, let us look at the case where the domain, T, is the vector space V, and the function space, S, is the dual space, $\hat{V}$.

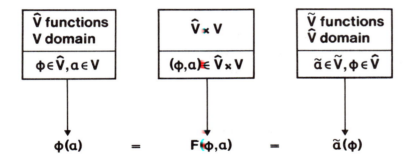

For any vector $\alpha \in V$, we get a function $\tilde{\alpha}$ with domain $\hat{V}$ and codomain R. What makes duality " tick " as far as vector spaces are concerned is this. $\hat{V}$ is a vector space and so there is no reason why we should not form its dual space—the space of all linear functionals on $\hat{V}$. We write $\hat{\hat{V}}$ (pronounced " V double hat " or V double cap ") for this space. The remarkable thing is that $\tilde{\alpha}$ turns out to be an element of $\hat{\hat{V}}$, i.e. a *linear functional* on $\hat{V}$. We ask you to prove this fact in the next exercise.

Theorem 4

For any $\alpha \in V$, define the function

$$\tilde{\alpha} : \hat{V} \longrightarrow R,$$

by

$$\tilde{\alpha}(\phi) = \phi(\alpha) \qquad (\phi \in \hat{V}).$$

Then $\tilde{\alpha}$ is a linear functional on $\hat{V}$.

Exercise

Prove Theorem 4.

Solution

We know that $\phi(\alpha) \in R$, and so $\tilde{\alpha}$ certainly maps $\tilde{V}$ to R. It remains to show that $\tilde{\alpha}$ is linear, i.e. that $\tilde{\alpha}(a\phi + b\psi) = a\tilde{\alpha}(\phi) + b\tilde{\alpha}(\psi)$, for $a, b \in R$ and $\phi, \psi \in \tilde{V}$.

$$\tilde{\alpha}(a\phi + b\psi) = (a\phi + b\psi)(\alpha) \qquad \text{(by the definition of } \tilde{\alpha})$$

$$= (a\phi)(\alpha) + (b\psi)(\alpha) \qquad \text{(by the definition of addition of functions)}$$

$$= a\phi(\alpha) + b\psi(\alpha)$$

$$= a\tilde{\alpha}(\phi) + b\tilde{\alpha}(\psi), \qquad \text{as required.}$$

We have just seen that $\tilde{\alpha}$ is a linear functional on $\tilde{V}$. That is to say, it is an element of $\hat{V}$. So the $\tilde{V}$ in the figure above is really a subset of $\hat{V}$.

Exercise

(i)   Let $\alpha = (1, 2)$, $\phi = [3\ 4]$. Calculate $\tilde{\alpha}(\phi)$.

(ii) Calculate $\tilde{\alpha}([a\ b])$ for any $a, b \in R$.

(iii) Let $\beta = (5, 6)$. Calculate $\tilde{\beta}([3\ 4])$.

(iv) Calculate $(2\alpha + 3\beta)\tilde{\ }([3\ 4])$.

(v) Calculate $(2\alpha + 3\beta)\tilde{\ }([a\ b])$ for any $a, b \in R$.

Solution

$$\text{(i)} \quad \tilde{\alpha}(\phi) = \phi(\alpha) = [3\ 4]\begin{bmatrix} 1 \\ 2 \end{bmatrix}$$

$$= 11.$$

$$\text{(ii)} \quad \tilde{\alpha}([a\ b]) = [a\ b]\begin{bmatrix} 1 \\ 2 \end{bmatrix}$$

$$= a + 2b.$$

$$\text{(iii)} \quad \tilde{\beta}([3\ 4]) = [3\ 4]\begin{bmatrix} 5 \\ 6 \end{bmatrix}$$

$$= 39.$$

$$\text{(iv)} \quad (2\alpha + 3\beta)\tilde{\ }([3\ 4]) = [3\ 4]\left(2\begin{bmatrix} 1 \\ 2 \end{bmatrix} + 3\begin{bmatrix} 5 \\ 6 \end{bmatrix}\right)$$

$$= [3\ 4]\begin{bmatrix} 17 \\ 22 \end{bmatrix}$$

$$= 139.$$

$$\text{(v)} \quad (2\alpha + 3\beta)\tilde{\ }([a\ b]) = [a\ b]\left(2\begin{bmatrix} 1 \\ 2 \end{bmatrix} + 3\begin{bmatrix} 5 \\ 6 \end{bmatrix}\right)$$

$$= [a\ b]\begin{bmatrix} 17 \\ 22 \end{bmatrix}$$

$$= 17a + 22b.$$

Although in the above exercise we did not show that $(2\alpha + 3\beta)\tilde{\ } = 2\tilde{\alpha} + 3\tilde{\beta}$, it is in fact the case, as we shall see in the next sub-section.

12.2.3 Is $\tilde{V}$ the whole of $\hat{\hat{V}}$?

We have seen that $\tilde{V}$ is a subset of $\hat{\hat{V}}$. When V is finite-dimensional, we can establish the fact that $\tilde{V} = \hat{\hat{V}}$ by showing that they have the same dimension, and invoking Theorem 4.7 on page N22.*

The easiest way to show that dim $\tilde{V} = $ dim $\hat{\hat{V}}$ is to show that dim $\tilde{V} = $ dim V; for we can apply Theorem 2 twice to get the result

$$\dim V = \dim \hat{V} = \dim \hat{\hat{V}}.$$

We have a mapping from V to $\hat{\hat{V}}$ that takes α to $\tilde{\alpha}$. If we label this mapping J, we have

$$J : \alpha \longmapsto \tilde{\alpha} \qquad (\alpha \in V)$$

where

$$\tilde{\alpha}(\phi) = \phi(\alpha) \qquad (\phi \in \hat{V})$$

and $\tilde{V}$ is the image set $J(V)$. If we can prove that J is a linear transformation, then we can use the Dimension Theorem (Theorem 1.6, page N31):

$$\dim J(V) + \dim K(J) = \dim V$$

where $K(J)$ is the kernel of J. If dim $K(J)$ turns out to be zero, then we have the result we are looking for, and we can assert that dim $\tilde{V} = $ dim $\hat{\hat{V}}$, and that J is an isomorphism of V onto $\hat{\hat{V}}$.

Theorem 5

If dim V is finite, then (i) dim $\tilde{V} = $ dim $\hat{\hat{V}}$, and (ii) J is an isomorphism of V onto $\hat{\hat{V}}$.

Proof

We first show that J is a linear transformation, i.e. that

$$J(a\alpha + b\beta) = aJ(\alpha) + bJ(\beta)$$

for any vectors $\alpha, \beta \in V$ and any scalars a, b.

To calculate $J(a\alpha + b\beta)$, we calculate its effect on an arbitrary element ϕ of $\hat{V}$.

$$\begin{aligned}
(J(a\alpha + b\beta))(\phi) &= (a\alpha + b\beta)^{\tilde{}}(\phi) \\
&= \phi(a\alpha + b\beta) \\
&= a\phi(\alpha) + b\phi(\beta) \\
&= a\tilde{\alpha}(\phi) + b\tilde{\beta}(\phi) \\
&= a(J(\alpha))(\phi) + b(J(\beta))(\phi).
\end{aligned}$$

This is true for all $\phi \in \hat{V}$, so

$$J(a\alpha + b\beta) = aJ(\alpha) + bJ(\beta) \qquad (a, b \in R; \alpha, \beta \in V).$$

Next we show that $K(J) = 0$.

Suppose $J(\alpha) = 0$. Then

$$(J(\alpha))(\phi) = 0 \text{ for all } \phi \in \hat{V}$$

i.e.

$$\tilde{\alpha}(\phi) = 0 \text{ for all } \phi \in \hat{V}$$

i.e.

$$\phi(\alpha) = 0 \text{ for all } \phi \in \hat{V}$$

---

* This Theorem has not been covered in a reading passage, but you should be able to follow N's proof.

But if $\alpha \neq 0$, it can form the first element, α_1, of a basis of V, in which case if ϕ_1 is the first element of the dual basis, then $\phi_1(\alpha_1) = 1$. Thus, since $\phi(\alpha) = 0$ for all $\phi \in \hat{V}$, we cannot have $\alpha \neq 0$. That is,

$$\alpha = 0.$$

Thus $K(J) = 0$.

We can now establish part (i) of the theorem. Since $K(J) = 0$, dim $K(J) = 0$ and the Dimension Theorem yields, since $\tilde{V} = J(V)$,

$$\text{dim } \tilde{V} = \text{dim } V$$

and hence (applying Theorem 2 twice)

$$\text{dim } \tilde{V} = \text{dim } \hat{V}.$$

To establish part (ii) we use Theorem 4.7 on page N22, which implies:

Theorem 6

$\tilde{V}$ is the whole of $\hat{V}$ (i.e. J is onto $\hat{V}$) if V is finite-dimensional.

Hence, since $K(J) = 0$, J is one-to-one, and so J is an isomorphism of V onto $\hat{V}$. The mapping J is just the correspondence between linear functionals on $\hat{V}$ and vectors in V which we set up using matrices in sub-section 12.2.1, but now it has been defined in a basis-independent fashion. J is, in fact, completely basis-independent, i.e. it is a *natural isomorphism* between V and $\hat{V}$. It resembles other basis-independent concepts, such as dimension, in this respect. There are, of course, any number of isomorphisms between V and $\hat{V}$, and for that matter between V and $\hat{V}$, as they all have the same number of dimensions. But J stands out from these, in a way in which no other isomorphism from V to $\hat{V}$, and no isomorphism at all from V to $\hat{V}$, does, in being defined in basis-independent terms.

Exercises

1. Exercise 1, page N134. (*Hint*: have you solved a problem like this before ? Look at Exercise 5, page N132, which you did as Exercise 3, in sub-section 12.1.3.)

2. List some intrinsic, i.e., basis-independent, properties of linear transformations that we have met in this course.

Solutions

1. This is the dual of Exercise 3 of sub-section 12.1.3. Thus:

Solution 3, sub-section 12.1.3	Solution of the present problem
Let $\alpha = \sum_{j=1}^{n} a_j \alpha_j$.	Let $\phi = \sum_{j=1}^{n} a_j \phi_j$.
$\phi_i(\alpha) = \phi_i\left(\sum_{j=1}^{n} a_j \alpha_j\right)$	$\phi(\alpha_i) = \left(\sum_{j=1}^{n} a_j \phi_j\right)(\alpha_i)$
$= \sum_{j=1}^{n} a_j \phi_i(\alpha_j)$	$= \sum_{j=1}^{n} a_j \phi_j(\alpha_i)$
$= \sum_{j=1}^{n} a_j \delta_{ij}$	$= \sum_{j=1}^{n} a_j \delta_{ij}$
$= a_i$.	$= a_i$.
That is, $\phi_i(\alpha) = a_i$.	That is, $\phi(\alpha_i) = a_i$.
Thus, $\alpha = \sum_{i=1}^{n} a_i \alpha_i$	Thus, $\phi = \sum_{i=1}^{n} a_i \phi_i$
$= \sum_{i=1}^{n} \phi_i(\alpha)\alpha_i$.	$= \sum_{i=1}^{n} \phi(\alpha_i)\phi_i$.

2. The major intrinsic properties we have met are as follows. In *Unit 2, Linear Transformations* we met the three "vital statistics" of a linear transformation: dimension of domain, rank (dimension of image space), dimension of codomain, which are intrinsic; so is the nullity (dimension of the kernel), which is dependent on the first two above, the dependence being expressed in the Dimension Theorem. If the transformation is an endomorphism, it has further intrinsic properties: its eigenvalues, invariant subspaces, and the related properties introduced in *Unit 5, Determinants and Eigenvalues* such as eigenvectors, eigenspaces, characteristic polynomial. Other intrinsic properties are those discussed in *Unit 10, Jordan Normal Form*; for example, Jordan normal form itself. There are many other properties with which by now we are very familiar; e.g., the image of a vector space is a vector space, the image of the zero vector is the zero vector, the kernel is a subspace of the domain, etc.

The intimacy of the relationship between V and $\hat{V}$ is further revealed when we look for a basis in $\hat{V}$. For example, if V is two-dimensional (and therefore so are $\hat{V}$ and $\hat{\hat{V}}$), suppose V, $\hat{V}$ and $\hat{\hat{V}}$ have bases:

$$A = \{\alpha_1, \alpha_2\}; \qquad \hat{A} = \{\phi_1, \phi_2\}; \qquad \hat{\hat{A}} = \{\lambda_1, \lambda_2\},$$

where $\hat{A}$ is the dual basis to A and $\hat{\hat{A}}$ is the dual basis to $\hat{A}$. Then we can find $\hat{\hat{A}}$ in terms of A as follows.

The definition of dual basis (sub-section 12.1.3) gives

$$\phi_i(\alpha_j) = \delta_{ij}, \text{ i.e.} \begin{cases} \phi_1(\alpha_1) = 1 & \phi_1(\alpha_2) = 0 \\ \phi_2(\alpha_1) = 0 & \phi_2(\alpha_2) = 1 \end{cases} \tag{1}$$

and

$$\lambda_i(\phi_j) = \delta_{ij}, \text{ i.e.} \begin{cases} \lambda_1(\phi_1) = 1 & \lambda_1(\phi_2) = 0 \\ \lambda_2(\phi_1) = 0 & \lambda_2(\phi_2) = 1 \end{cases} \tag{2}$$

We have

$$\tilde{\alpha}_1(\phi_1) = \phi(\alpha_1) \qquad (\phi \in \hat{V}) \tag{3}$$

Putting $\phi = \phi_1$, then $\phi = \phi_2$, in Equation (3) gives

$$\tilde{\alpha}_1(\phi) = \phi_1(\alpha_1) = 1, \quad \tilde{\alpha}_1(\phi_2) = \phi_2(\alpha_1) = 0$$

Similarly

$$\tilde{\alpha}_2(\phi_1) = \phi_1(\alpha_2) = 0, \quad \tilde{\alpha}_2(\phi_2) = \phi_2(\alpha_2) = 1 \tag{4}$$

Comparing Equations (2) with Equations (4), we see that $\tilde{\alpha}_1 = \lambda_1$, as they are equal on the elements $\{\phi_1, \phi_2\}$ of a basis of $\hat{V}$, and similarly $\tilde{\alpha}_2 = \lambda_2$. That is to say,

$$\{\lambda_1, \lambda_2\} = \{\tilde{\alpha}_1, \tilde{\alpha}_2\}$$
$$\hat{\hat{A}} = \{\tilde{\alpha}_1, \tilde{\alpha}_2\}$$
$$= \{J(\alpha_1), J(\alpha_2)\}.$$

To put it another way, with respect to bases A of V and $\hat{\hat{A}}$ of $\hat{\hat{V}}$, the matrix representing J is the identity matrix. This is true *whatever* basis A we start off with, and is another way of looking at the "naturalness" of the correspondence J between V and $\hat{\hat{V}}$.

12.2.4 Summary of Section 12.2

In this section we defined the term

      natural isomorphism   (page **C**29)   ★

Theorems

4. (page **C**26)
For any $\alpha \in V$, let $\tilde{\alpha}(\phi) = \phi(\alpha)$ for all $\phi \in \hat{V}$; then $\tilde{\alpha}$ is a linear functional on $\hat{V}$.   ★ ★ ★

5. (page **C**28)
If dim V is finite, then (i) dim $\tilde{V} = $ dim $\hat{V}$, and (ii) J is an isomorphism of V onto $\hat{V}$.   ★ ★ ★

6. (page **C**29)
$\tilde{V}$ is the whole of $\hat{V}$ if V is finite-dimensional.   ★ ★ ★

Notation

     $\tilde{\alpha}$ (page **C**26)
     $\hat{V}$ (page **C**26)
     $\tilde{V}$ (page **C**26)

READ Section IV-2, starting on page **N**133.

Note   *Paragraph following the proof of Theorem 2.1 on pages* **N**133–4.

What Nering means here is that in the infinite-dimensional case the concept of *continuity* of a function over V is very much more subtle than in the finite-dimensional case. Several different definitions can be given of what it could mean for such a function to be "continuous", and the particular definition chosen depends on the exact use to which the infinite-dimensional space is being put. If one restricts the definition of the "dual" of such a space by saying that it consists of all *continuous* linear functionals, then the definition of continuity will affect the size of the dual (and hence of $\hat{V}$ the double dual); some definitions will make the double dual equal to the original space, and others will not.

12.3 DUALITY IN ACTION

12.3.0 Introduction

Our discussion in the Introduction to the unit of greengrocers and their customers was designed to help you to understand what a dual space is, rather than to show you the idea of duality being used. This unit will not help you next time you go shopping, and you may well be asking "what use is the concept of duality to anybody who actually uses mathematics?" In the first two sub-sections of this section we will try to give you the beginnings of an answer to this question, and to show you how mathematical *ideas* can be just as useful to the development of a science as mathematical *calculations*. Both these sub-sections are *optional*; the second, on the "delta function", is one that you may find rather difficult, and you may wish to come back to it for interest when you have some time to spare later in the course.

Sub-section 12.3.3 returns to the pursuit of mathematics central to the development of the course, and discusses the concept of an *annihilator*. An annihilator is really a solution set of a system of homogeneous linear equations, but new insight is gained by looking at it from the standpoint of duality. This is an *important* section, as the material in it is used later in the course, in *Unit 15, Affine Geometry and Convex Cones*.

12.3.1 Factor Analysis (Optional)

We take our first example from psychology. Here even more than in the physical sciences, linear models are no more than approximations, often very rough approximations.

The pioneers of the kind of psychology that attempts measurements on the natures of living organisms rather than speculations on the Nature of Life, were probably Pavlov and Watson, who used the "stimulus-response" model. That is to say, they considered animals (and people) as things that respond to external stimuli, in a predictable way.

$$\xrightarrow{\text{stimulus}} \boxed{\text{animal}} \xrightarrow{\text{response}}$$

In mathematical language, the animal may be considered as a function whose domain is the set of all stimuli, and whose codomain is the set of all responses. However, it is rather difficult to see how to give any mathematical structure, in this model, to "the set of all stimuli"; and no consistent account was taken of the differences in response between different animals (or people). In fact, Watson assumed that there were no inherent differences between animals of a given species (e.g. people), and that all observed differences consisted merely of different ways in which the environment had forced the various possible stimuli and responses together, to form "conditioned responses".

A major advance was made during the first half of this century, with the recognition that (especially where people are concerned) differences between one person and another are of great importance, and could be quantified. The statistical techniques of *factor analysis** allow these differences to be expressed within a vector space model. The idea is that various *factors* (intelligence, extraversion, tenacity, etc.) vary independently from person to person, and by a series of tests it is possible (within a certain degree of accuracy) to measure people on the various scales. But how are we to decide exactly what to measure? The answer is that we construct a wide variety of tests, record a number of people's scores on these, and analyse

---

* The following book contains a good discussion of factor analysis: D.N. Lawley and A. E. Maxwell, *Factor Analysis as a Statistical Method* (Butterworth, 1963).

the results to see just how many dimensions the vector space needs to have, in order to account (again, to within a specified degree of accuracy) for the variation observed in the scores people obtain.

The model that is used assumes that a person's performance on a given test will depend *linearly* on the degree to which he possesses various factors. For instance, if the test is his ability to play tennis, it *might* be found that this ability (A) depends to a great extent on the amount of practice he has had (P), to a lesser extent on his intelligence (I), and to a lesser extent still on his "tenacity" (T). We might have

$$A = 0.5P + 0.3I + 0.2T$$

so that ability to play tennis is a linear functional, with matrix representation

[0.5 0.3 0.2],

on the vector space describing people.

Having worked out a consistent way of measuring people, we can "measure" new "tests" against the vector space which measures the people. Ability to fly a lunar module, for instance, might require a great deal of tenacity, slightly less intelligence, and make no demands at all on how much practice a person has had at tennis. Perhaps it would correspond to the matrix [0 0.7 0.8]. In order to discover the various factors required, one would simulate a lunar module and test various people whose characteristics (intelligence, etc.) were already known. In effect, one would be working out how to place the test of "flying a lunar module" in a vector space of possible tests, and one would be regarding people with various levels of measured intelligence, tenacity, etc., as linear functionals on this vector space.

We thus have a complete duality between the characteristics of people and the situations in which they are placed. If we postulate a certain mathematical structure for one, we must postulate a dual structure for the other, and each is equally important as an object of study for the psychologist.

12.3.2 The Delta Function (Optional)

This will probably be quite a difficult example to follow, but well worth the effort. It shows that the idea of a function can be generalized to include a class of objects that are not themselves functions, but may in a sense be "limits" of infinite sequences of functions. These generalized functions first arose in the work of the theoretical physicist, P. A. M. Dirac, in 1929, but it was not until 1945 that the mathematician L. Schwartz showed that they could be put on a rigorous footing using the concept of a linear functional. (There is a brief discussion of the same idea at the top of page **K222**.)

This generalization comes about as a result of the fact that we can map a space of functions, such as $C[0, 1]$ (the vector space of real-valued continuous functions on $[0, 1]$), into its dual space, by means of integration. That is to say, corresponding to every function g in $C[0, 1]$, we can define a linear functional L_g on $C[0, 1]$, by

$$L_g : f \longmapsto \int_0^1 f(t)g(t)\, dt \qquad (f \in C[0, 1]).$$

We should check that L_g is really a linear functional. The domain and codomain are certainly right; so we have to make sure that L_g maps the domain ($C[0, 1]$) *linearly* to the codomain R. This follows directly from the rules of integration (see *Unit M100 13, Integration II*):

$$L_g(af_1 + bf_2) = \int_0^1 (af_1 + bf_2)(t)g(t)\, dt$$

$$= \int_0^1 (af_1(t)g(t) + bf_2(t)g(t))\, dt$$

$$= a \int_0^1 f_1(t)g(t)\, dt + b \int_0^1 f_2(t)g(t)\, dt$$

$$= aL_g(f_1) + bL_g(f_2).$$

Now the mapping L which takes g to L_g for every g in $C[0, 1]$, is itself a linear transformation, from $C[0, 1]$ to its dual. We can show this as follows. For every g in $C[0, 1]$, L_g is a linear functional on $C[0, 1]$. Thus the domain and codomain are right, and we have to make sure that L is linear. That is to say, let g_1, g_2 be arbitrary elements of $C[0, 1]$ and a, b arbitrary real numbers; then we have to show that

$$L_{ag_1 + bg_2} = aL_{g_1} + bL_{g_2}$$

To show this, we compute the effects of $L_{ag_1 + bg_2}$ on an arbitrary element f of $C[0, 1]$.

$$L_{ag_1 + bg_2}(f) = \int_0^1 f(t)(ag_1 + bg_2)(t)\, dt$$

$$= \int_0^1 f(t)(ag_1(t) + bg_2(t))\, dt$$

$$= a \int_0^1 f(t)g_1(t)\, dt + b \int_0^1 f(t)g_2(t)\, dt$$

$$= aL_{g_1}(f) + bL_{g_2}(f).$$

Since this equality holds for all $f \in C[0, 1]$, we conclude that

$$L_{ag_1 + bg_2} = aL_{g_1} + bL_{g_2} \qquad (g_1, g_2 \in C[0, 1]; a, b \in R).$$

Thus L is linear.

Now things do not go as smoothly in infinite-dimensional spaces as they do in finite-dimensional spaces.* We have just proved that L is a linear transformation of $C[0, 1]$ into its own dual, but we said nothing about its being an *isomorphism*. (In finite-dimensional spaces, we know that V is isomorphic to $\hat{V}$, since they have the same dimension.) There is a good reason for this L is *not* an isomorphism of $C[0, 1]$ with its own dual, and in fact there is no isomorphism of $C[0, 1]$ with its own dual. So what goes wrong?

The answer is that there are a vast number of elements of the dual of $C[0, 1]$ that are *not* images of elements of $C[0, 1]$ under L. Consider for instance, the mapping

$$P_{1/2} : f \longmapsto f(\tfrac{1}{2}) \qquad (f \in C[0, 1]).$$

This is the same sort of mapping as in Exercise 1(d) of sub-section 12.1.1, and is easily seen to be a linear functional. But there is no function g such that

$$L_g = P_{1/2}.$$

To see this, try to imagine how the integral

$$\int_0^1 f(t)g(t)\, dt$$

varies as f varies and g remains fixed. It is intuitively clear that, in any region where g takes non-zero values, the value of the integral will be affected by altering the values which f takes in that region. On the other hand, the value of $P_{1/2}(f)$ is affected *only* by the value of f at $\tfrac{1}{2}$; f can take on any values it likes at other points without affecting the value of $P_{1/2}(f)$. On the other hand, $P_{1/2}$ is not entirely unconnected with functions in $C[0, 1]$; it is in some sense the *limit* of a sequence of functionals

$$L_{g_1}, L_{g_2}, \ldots,$$

where $g_1, g_2, \ldots \in C[0, 1]$. We can construct a suitable sequence $g_1, g_2, \ldots$ by using the following idea. The value of $P_{1/2}(f)$ is affected only by the function value at $\tfrac{1}{2}$, so can we select functions $g_1, g_2, \ldots$ which narrow down the range of points in $[0, 1]$ within which the value of f affects the value of $L_g(f)$? The answer is that we *can* do this, by requiring that the functions $g_1, g_2, \ldots$ differ from zero only on certain sub-intervals of $[0, 1]$. We can, for instance, demand that

$$g_n(x) = 0 \qquad (x \notin [\tfrac{1}{2} - 2^{-n}, \tfrac{1}{2} + 2^{-n}])$$

and that $g_n(x)$ be constructed *within* the interval $[\tfrac{1}{2} - 2^{-n}, \tfrac{1}{2} + 2^{-n}]$ in such a way that

$$\int_0^1 g_n(x)\, dx = \int_{(1/2)-2^{-n}}^{(1/2)+2^{-n}} g_n(x)\, dx \qquad (1)$$
$$= 1$$

and

$$g_n(x) \geqslant 0 \qquad (x \in [0, 1]).$$

Some g_n are illustrated on the next page.

* See the last paragraph on page N133.

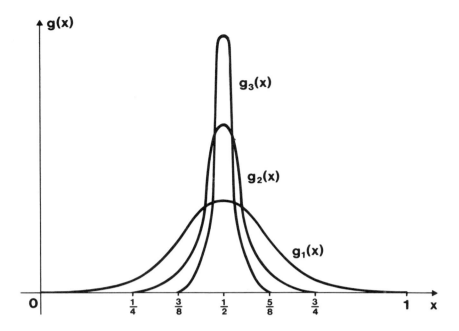

Now what about $L_{g_n}(f)$? We have specifically imposed condition (1) in $g_n(x)$ so that

$$\lim_{n \text{ large}} (L_{g_n}(f)) = f(\tfrac{1}{2}).$$

Can you see why this should be so?

The reason is as follows. If we let c_n be the minimum value of $f(x)$ in the interval $[\tfrac{1}{2} - 2^{-n}, \tfrac{1}{2} + 2^{-n}]$, and d_n the maximum value in this interval, then

$$\int_0^1 c_n g_n(x)\, dx \leqslant \int_0^1 f(x) g_n(x)\, dx \leqslant \int_0^1 d_n g_n(x)\, dx$$

i.e.

$$c_n \leqslant L_{g_n}(f) \leqslant d_n.$$

Now, because f is continuous, and because the width of the interval $[\tfrac{1}{2} - 2^{-n}, \tfrac{1}{2} + 2^{-n}]$ approaches zero, we must have

$$\lim_{n \text{ large}} c_n = f(\tfrac{1}{2}) = \lim_{n \text{ large}} d_n.$$

Thus,

$$\lim_{n \text{ large}} L_{g_n}(f) = f(\tfrac{1}{2}) = P_{1/2}(f).$$

(Of course, we have omitted a number of points of mathematical detail here, so as to give you a general idea of what is happening. To do it properly would require much more time and space.)

Thus $\lim\limits_{n \text{ large}} L_{g_n}$ is a perfectly well-defined linear functional on $C[0, 1]$. However, $\lim\limits_{n \text{ large}} g_n$ is not a function from $[0, 1]$ to R in any normal sense. If you look at the diagram again, you will see that

$$\lim_{n \text{ large}} g_n(x) = 0, \quad \text{when } x \neq \tfrac{1}{2},$$

since the intervals on which the g_n are non-zero rapidly become narrower and narrower, and eventually exclude the point x if $x \neq \tfrac{1}{2}$.

But

$\lim\limits_{n \text{ large}} g_n(\tfrac{1}{2})$ does not exist; somehow $g_n(\tfrac{1}{2})$ " goes to infinity ", so if we wish to picture $\lim\limits_{n \text{ large}} (g_n)$ as a function, it must be a function which is "equal to infinity" at $\tfrac{1}{2}$, and zero everywhere else! Physicists often find such an idea useful as a mental picture, but clearly such an idea is not *mathematically* satisfactory. To be mathematically sound, we should express $P_{1/2}$ simply in terms of its effects on elements f of $C[0, 1]$, which, of course, we can do perfectly well.

So we see that we have generalized the notion of a function, and ended up in the dual space to a space of functions. This is no academic exercise; as we have said, physicists in the first half of this century were faced with exactly this problem.

To get an inkling of the sort of situation in which the problem arises, look back to sub-section 11.2.1 of *Unit 11, Differential Equations III*. We saw there that a particular solution of the normal linear differential equation

$$L(y) = h \tag{2}$$

can be expressed by the formula

$$y_p(x) = \int_{x_0}^{x} K(x, t)h(t)\, dt \tag{3}$$

where $K(x, t)$ is a certain function of two real variables. Equation (3) defines a linear transformation on the appropriate function space, under which the image of the function h is the function y_p. However, there are circumstances in which h is not a function in the usual sense, and yet a solution of $L(y) = h$ is known to exist. If $L(y) = h$ represents a mechanical system, for instance, with springs, weights, etc., then we might know that at a time t_0 the system was banged with a hammer, setting it suddenly into motion. The motion of the system is determined by L and h, where h would then be related to the impulse that the system received through being banged. But the assumption that it was banged with a hammer would mean that $h(t)$ would be zero whenever t was different from t_0, yet the integral (3) would be non-zero. In fact, h would be a "generalized function" of the sort we have just seen. Symbolically, a generalized function like the above is denoted by δ_{t_0} (the "Dirac delta function"). It is a function of t such that $\delta_{t_0}(t)$ is thought of as infinite at $t = t_0$ and equal to zero everywhere else, but only makes sense when it comes after an integral sign, or as the non-homogeneous part of a differential equation. In the case quoted above, Equations (2) and (3) would become:

$$L(y) = \delta_{t_0}(t) \tag{2a}$$

$$y_p(x) = \int_{x_0}^{x} K(x, t)\delta_{t_0}(t)\, dt \tag{3a}$$

12.3.3 Annihilators

In this sub-section we will take a brief look at another example of duality arising out of vector space theory: the concept of an *annihilator*. It is an important concept for you to grasp, as it is used later in the course (*Unit 15, Affine Geometry and Convex Cones*).

Definition

If S is any subset of a vector space V, then the *annihilator* of S is the following subset of $\hat{V}$ (denoted by $S^\perp$):

$$S^\perp = \{\phi \in \hat{V}: \phi(\alpha) = 0 \text{ for all } \alpha \in S\}.$$

($S^\perp$ is read as: "S-perp".)

This is a very broad definition: S can be *any* subset of V. In particular, S can be a *subspace* of V.

Example 1

Let $V = R^3$, $S = \langle(1, 0, 0), (0, 1, 0)\rangle$, i.e. S is the subspace of V generated by the first two basis elements of the standard basis. Then:

$$S^\perp = \{\phi \in \hat{V}: \phi(\alpha) = 0 \text{ for all } \alpha \text{ of the form } (a, b, 0) \in V\}.$$

Thus to find $S^\perp$, we must look for the set of all $[x\ y\ z]$ such that

$$[x\ y\ z]\begin{bmatrix} a \\ b \\ 0 \end{bmatrix} = 0 \text{ for all } a, b \in R,$$

i.e.

$$xa + yb = 0 \text{ for all } a, b \in R. \tag{1}$$

This condition places no restrictions on z, but clearly x and y must each be equal to zero for Equation (1) to hold for *all* $a, b \in R$.

Thus,

$$S^\perp = \{[0\ 0\ z] : z \in R\}$$
$$= \langle[0\ 0\ 1]\rangle.$$

We can see here why we use the $\perp$ (perpendicular) sign. The elements $[0\ 0\ z]$ are not in V, but if we ignore the type of brackets, the elements $(0, 0, z)$ lie along the z-axis representation of R^3, which is perpendicular to the (x, y)-plane representation of $\langle(1, 0, 0), (0, 1, 0)\rangle$. But, in spite of the suggestion, we must remember that $S^\perp$ and S are not in the same space.

Example 2

Let $V = R^3$ and let $S = \{(1, 0, 0), (0, 1, 0)\}$. That is, S is the set containing these two elements, not the subspace spanned by these two elements as in Example 1.

Then $\phi \in S^\perp$ if and only if

$$\phi((1, 0, 0)) = \phi((0, 1, 0)) = 0.$$

That is, $[x\ y\ z] \in S^\perp$ if and only if

$$[x\ y\ z]\begin{bmatrix} 1 \\ 0 \\ 0 \end{bmatrix} = [x\ y\ z]\begin{bmatrix} 0 \\ 1 \\ 0 \end{bmatrix} = 0,$$

i.e. if and only if $x = y = 0$.

Once again, then,

$$S^\perp = \{[0 \ 0 \ z] : z \in R\}$$
$$= \langle [0 \ 0 \ 1] \rangle.$$

In other words, although this time S is not a subspace of V, we still find that $S^\perp$ is a sub-space of $\hat{V}$.

Example 3

Let $V = R^3$, and let $S = \{(1, 2, 3), (1, 1, 1)\}$. Then $[x \ y \ z] \in S^\perp$ if and only if

$$[x \ y \ z]\begin{bmatrix} 1 \\ 2 \\ 3 \end{bmatrix} = [x \ y \ z]\begin{bmatrix} 1 \\ 1 \\ 1 \end{bmatrix} = 0$$

i.e., if and only if,

$$x + 2y + 3z = 0$$
$$x + \ y + \ z = 0$$

This should make it clear that an annihilator is really an old friend in a new disguise: it is the solution set of a system of homogeneous linear equations, i.e. of a "homogeneous linear problem" (*Unit 3*, pages N63–4). The only difference is that we regard it as being a subset of $\hat{V}$ rather than a subset of V. You already know that the solution set of a homogeneous linear problem is a subspace, so it should not be difficult to translate this knowledge into the language of the present unit, and fill in the gaps in the proof of the following theorem.

Theorem 7

If S is any subset of V, then $S^\perp$ is a subspace of $\hat{V}$.

Proof

We have to prove that, for all $a, b \in R$, and $\phi, \psi \in S^\perp$:

$$\underline{\hspace{4cm}} \in S^\perp \tag{i}$$

That is to say, we must show that if α is any element of S,

$$(\underline{\hspace{3cm}}) \, (\alpha) = \underline{\hspace{2cm}} \tag{ii}$$

We proceed:

$$(\underline{\hspace{3.5cm}})(\alpha) = \underline{\hspace{1cm}}\phi(\alpha) + \underline{\hspace{1cm}}\psi(\alpha) \tag{iii}$$

$$= \underline{\hspace{1.2cm}} + \underline{\hspace{1.2cm}} \tag{iv}$$

$$= \underline{\hspace{1cm}} \tag{v}$$

and the theorem is proved.

The lines with blanks should read as follows:

(i) $a\phi + b\psi \in S^\perp$ (ii) $(a\phi + b\psi)(\alpha) = 0$
(iii) $(a\phi + b\psi)(\alpha) = a\phi(\alpha) + b\psi(\alpha)$
(iv) $= 0 + 0$
(v) $= 0$

Another thing you will notice by comparing Examples 1 and 2, is that in this particular case the annihilator of $\{(1, 0, 0), (0, 1, 0)\}$ is equal to the annihilator of the subspace which they generate. This is another result which is true in general, and is stated in the next theorem.

Theorem 8

If S is any subset of a finite-dimensional space V, then $S^\perp = \langle S \rangle^\perp$.

Proof

Every element of $\langle S \rangle^\perp$ is contained in $S^\perp$, since if $\phi(\alpha) = 0$ for all $\alpha \in \langle S \rangle$, it is certainly zero for all $\alpha \in S$.

Conversely, if ϕ is any element of $S^\perp$ then the following argument shows that it is also in $\langle S \rangle^\perp$.

Let $\alpha \in \langle S \rangle$; we have to show that $\phi(\alpha) = 0$. Since $\langle S \rangle$ is generated by S, we can find elements $\alpha_1, \ldots, \alpha_k$ of S and scalars $a_1, \ldots, a_k$, such that

$$\alpha = a_1 \alpha_1 + \cdots + a_k \alpha_k$$

Then

$$\begin{aligned}
\phi(\alpha) &= \phi(a_1 \alpha_1 + \cdots + a_k \alpha_k) \\
&= a_1 \phi(\alpha_1) + \cdots + a_k \phi(\alpha_k) \\
&= 0 + \cdots + 0, \text{ since } \phi \in S^\perp, \\
&= 0,
\end{aligned}$$

and the theorem is proved.

Example 4

Find a basis for the annihilator $S^\perp$ of $S = \langle (2, 4, -1, 1, 2), (1, 2, 1, 8, 10) \rangle$. By Theorem 8, the annihilator of S is the same as the annihilator of the *set* $\{(2, 4, -1, 1, 2), (1, 2, 1, 8, 10)\}$. This is the set of linear functionals $[a\ b\ c\ d\ e]$ such that

$$\left.\begin{aligned}
2a + 4b - c + d + 2e &= 0, \\
a + 2b + c + 8d + 10e &= 0.
\end{aligned}\right\}$$

To solve this system of equations, we bring the matrix of coefficients to Hermite normal form; this results in the matrix

$$\begin{bmatrix} 1 & 2 & 0 & 3 & 4 \\ 0 & 0 & 1 & 5 & 6 \end{bmatrix}$$

corresponding to equations

$$\left.\begin{aligned}
a + 2b \quad + 3d + 4e &= 0, \\
c + 5d + 6e &= 0.
\end{aligned}\right\}$$

We can take b, d and e as arbitrary; this gives

$$\begin{aligned}
a &= -2b - 3d - 4e \\
c &= \quad\quad -5d - 6e
\end{aligned}$$

Thus

$$\begin{aligned}
[a\ b\ c\ d\ e] &= [(-2b - 3d - 4e)\ b\ (-5d - 6e)\ d\ e] \\
&= b[-2\ 1\ 0\ 0\ 0] + d[-3\ 0\ -5\ 1\ 0] \\
&\quad + e[-4\ 0\ -6\ 0\ 1].
\end{aligned}$$

Thus the required basis for $S^\perp$ is

$$\{[-2\ 1\ 0\ 0\ 0], [-3\ 0\ -5\ 1\ 0], [-4\ 0\ -6\ 0\ 1]\}.$$

Numerically, then, this calculation is equivalent to finding the kernel of the linear transformation represented by the 2×5 matrix

$$\begin{bmatrix} 2 & 4 & -1 & 1 & 2 \\ 1 & 2 & 1 & 8 & 10 \end{bmatrix}.$$

Exercises

1. In Example 4 above, the dimensions of S and $S^\perp$ add up to 5, the dimension of the original space. Does this always happen? Give a reason for your answer.

2. Calculate the set of all vectors $\alpha \in V$ such that $\phi(\alpha) = 0$ for all $\phi \in S^\perp$. How does this set relate to the annihilator of $S^\perp$, $(S^\perp)^\perp = S^{\perp\perp}$? (*Hint*: answer the second part of the question first. Then apply the Dimension Theorem to answer the first part.)

Solutions

1. Yes. The dimension of $S^\perp$ is the dimension of the kernel of the linear transformation from R^5 to R^2 represented by the matrix

$$\begin{bmatrix} 2 & 4 & -1 & 1 & 2 \\ 1 & 2 & 1 & 8 & 10 \end{bmatrix}.$$

On the other hand, the rows of this matrix represent the basis of S, and so the rank of the matrix is equal to the dimension of S. By the Dimension Theorem (*Unit 2*), these two dimensions must add up to the dimension of the entire domain space.

2. The annihilator of a subset of a space is in the dual of that space. Thus the annihilator of $S^\perp$ is in $\hat{\hat{V}}$, and is the set of all $\tilde{\alpha}$ in $\hat{\hat{V}}$ such that $\tilde{\alpha}(\phi) = 0$ for all $\phi \in S^\perp$. That is, if T is the set of all vectors $\alpha \in V$ such that $\phi(\alpha) = 0$ for all $\phi \in S^\perp$, then $S^{\perp\perp} = J(T)$, where J is the natural isomorphism of V with $\hat{\hat{V}}$ discussed in sub-section 12.2.3. It is usual, though, to ignore the isomorphism J altogether and regard V and $\hat{\hat{V}}$ as identical. Thus, we denote by $S^{\perp\perp}$ the set of all $\alpha \in V$ such that $\phi(\alpha) = 0$ for all $\phi \in S^\perp$.

   Using Theorem 8, we see that to calculate $S^{\perp\perp}$, we need to find the set of all $\alpha \in V$ such that $\phi_1(\alpha) = \phi_2(\alpha) = \phi_3(\alpha) = 0$, where $\{\phi_1, \phi_2, \phi_3\}$ is the basis of $S^\perp$ which we found in Solution 1. That is, we must find the set of all $\{v, w, x, y, z\}$ such that

$$\left. \begin{array}{l} -2v + w \qquad\qquad = 0, \\ -3v \qquad -5x + y \qquad = 0, \\ -4v \qquad -6x \qquad + z = 0. \end{array} \right\}$$

   Now we could find a basis of $S^{\perp\perp}$ by reducing the coefficient matrix of this system to Hermite normal form, but we can get the answer more quickly by using the Dimension Theorem in exactly the same way as in Solution 1. In other words, $S^\perp$ is 3-dimensional, so $S^{\perp\perp}$ must be 2-dimensional. Thus if we find two linearly independent elements of $S^{\perp\perp}$, they must form a basis for $S^{\perp\perp}$.

   What about our original basis of S? This was $\{(2, 4, -1, 1, 2), (1, 2, 1, 8, 10)\}$. Because $S^\perp$ annihilates S, it must be the case that $\phi(\alpha) = 0$ for all $\phi \in S^\perp$, if α is either $(2, 4, -1, 1, 2)$ or $(1, 2, 1, 8, 10)$. Therefore, these vectors do indeed form a basis for $S^{\perp\perp}$.

We finish this sub-section by writing out the results we have just discovered in a special case, in the form of theorems.

Theorem 9

If S is a subspace of a finite-dimensional space V, then $\dim S + \dim S^\perp = \dim V$.

Proof

Let S be k-dimensional, and V be n-dimensional. Let $\{\alpha_1, \ldots, \alpha_k\}$ be a basis of S; then it can be extended to a basis $\{\alpha_1, \ldots, \alpha_k, \alpha_{k+1}, \ldots, \alpha_n\}$ of V.

Let $\{\phi_1, \ldots, \phi_n\}$ be the basis of $\hat{V}$ dual to $\{\alpha_1, \ldots, \alpha_n\}$. Then any element ϕ of $\hat{V}$ is of the form

$$\phi = a_1\phi_1 + \cdots + a_n\phi_n,$$

and it is not difficult to check that $\phi(\alpha) = 0$ for all $\alpha \in S$, if and only if

$$a_1 = a_2 = \cdots = a_k = 0.$$

That is, $\phi \in S^\perp$ if and only if $a_1^* = c_2 = \cdots = a_k = 0$, which is the same as saying that $\{\phi_{k+1}, \ldots, \phi_n\}$ is a basis for $S^\perp$. Thus, $S^\perp$ is $(n-k)$-dimensional, and this proves the theorem.

Theorem 10

If S is a subspace of a finite-dimensional space V, then $S^{\perp\perp} = S$.

Proof

If $\alpha \in S$, then $\phi(\alpha) = 0$ for all $\phi \in S^\perp$, and so $\alpha \in S^{\perp\perp}$. Thus, $S \subset S^{\perp\perp}$.

But by Theorem 9,

$$\dim S + \dim S^\perp = \dim V,$$

and

$$\dim S^\perp + \dim S^{\perp\perp} = \dim \hat{V}$$
$$= \dim V,$$

and hence $\dim S^{\perp\perp} = \dim S$.

Therefore, $S = S^{\perp\perp}$ (see Theorem 4.7 on page N22).

Exercise

Exercise 3, page N141.

Solution

See page N333.

12.3.4 Summary of Section 12.3

In this section we defined the term

annihilator   (page C38)   ★ ★ ★

Theorems

7. (page C39)
If S is any subset of V, $S^\perp$ is a subspace of $\hat{V}$.   ★ ★ ★

8. (page C39)
If S is any subset of a finite-dimensional space V, then $S^\perp = \langle S \rangle^\perp$.   ★

9. (page C41)
If S is a subspace of a finite-dimensional space V, then $\dim S + \dim S^\perp = \dim V$.   ★

10. (page C42)
If S is a subspace of a finite-dimensional space V, then $S^{\perp\perp} = S$.   ★

Technique

Find a basis for the annihilator of a subset of V.   ★

Notation

$S^\perp$ (page C38)
$S^{\perp\perp}$ (page C41)

READ Section IV-4, starting on page N138 as far as the end of page N139.

12.4 SUMMARY OF THE UNIT

The aim of this unit is to introduce you to some powerful abstract mathematical ideas, namely those connected with the concepts of linear functionals and duality.

In the first section, we introduced the idea of linear functionals and discussed the structure of the space of all linear functionals on a vector space V, the dual space of V. We discovered that it is itself a vector space, of the same dimension as V and closely connected to it in structure.

In the second section we looked at the meaning of linear functionals on the dual space $\hat{V}$ and found that the dual space of $\hat{V}$ is naturally isomorphic to V itself. We also introduced the mapping J which establishes this natural isomorphism between vectors in V and linear functionals on $\hat{V}$.

The third section was used to illustrate the concept of dual space. The first example was a practical one in psychology—factor analysis. The second example was a theoretical one leading to the definition of the Dirac delta function. The last sub-section dealt with the annihilator, i.e. the set of linear functionals on V which will annihilate a given subset of V.

Definitions

linear functional	(page C5)	★ ★ ★
dual space	(page C10)	★ ★ ★
dual basis	(page C13)	★ ★ ★
natural isomorphism	(page C29)	★
annihilator	(page C38)	★ ★ ★

Theorems

1. (page C9)
The set of all linear functionals on V forms a vector space. ★ ★ ★

2. (page C11)
If V is n-dimensional, so is $\hat{V}$. ★ ★ ★

3. (page C18)
Let V be a vector space with basis A and let $\hat{A}$ be the dual basis in $\hat{V}$. If A' is a new basis of V and the matrix of transition from A to A' is P, then the coordinates of $\widehat{A'}$ with respect to $\hat{A}$ are the columns of Q, the matrix of transition from $\hat{A}$ to $\widehat{A'}$, and $Q = (P^{-1})^T$. ★

4. (page C26)
For any $\alpha \in V$, let $\tilde{\alpha}(\phi) = \phi(\alpha)$ for all $\phi \in \hat{V}$; then $\tilde{\alpha}$ is a linear functional on $\hat{V}$. ★ ★ ★

5. (page C28)
If dim V is finite, then (i) dim $\tilde{V} = $ dim $\hat{\hat{V}}$, and (ii) J is an isomorphism of V onto $\hat{\hat{V}}$. ★ ★ ★

6. (page C29)
$\tilde{V}$ is the whole of $\hat{\hat{V}}$ if V is finite-dimensional. ★ ★ ★

7. (page C39)
If S is any subset of V, $S^\perp$ is a subspace of $\hat{V}$. ★ ★ ★

8. (page C39)
If S is any subset of a finite-dimensional space V, then $S^\perp = \langle S \rangle^\perp$. ★

9. (page C41)
If S is a subspace of a finite-dimensional space V, then dim $S + $ dim $S^\perp = $ dim V. ★

10.   (page C42)
If S is a subspace of a finite-dimensional space V, then $S^{\perp\perp} = S$.   ⋆

Techniques

1.   Given a basis A of a vector space V, determine the corresponding dual   ⋆ ⋆ ⋆
basis A in the dual vector space $\hat{V}$.

2.   Find a basis for the annihilator of a subset of V.   ⋆

Notation

$[a\ b\ c\ ...]$	(page C9)
$\hat{V}$	(page C9)
$\hat{A}$	(page C13)
$\tilde{\alpha}$	(page C26)
$\hat{\hat{V}}$	(page C26)
$\tilde{V}$	(page C26)
$S^{\perp}$	(page C38)
$S^{\perp\perp}$	(page C41)

We can draw up a table to represent the concepts and their dual concepts,
that we have seen in this unit: this is another way to summarize the unit.

Concept	*Dual*
Vector Space V	Dual Space $\hat{V}$
Basis A	Dual basis $\hat{A}$
Subspace S of V	Annihilator $S^{\perp}$ in $\hat{V}$

12.5 SELF-ASSESSMENT

Self-assessment Test

This Self-assessment Test is designed to help you test quickly your understanding of the unit. It can also be used, together with the summary of the unit for revision. The answers to these questions will be found on the next non-facing page. We suggest you complete the whole test before looking at the answers.

1. (i) Which of the following are linear functionals? Give reasons for rejecting those that are not.

(a) $\phi : (x_1, x_2, x_3) \longmapsto \begin{bmatrix} x_1 \\ x_2 \\ x_3 \end{bmatrix}$ $((x_1, x_2, x_3) \in R^3)$

(b) $\phi : (x_1, x_2, x_3) \longmapsto 2x_1 + 3x_2$ $\quad ((x_1, x_2, x_3) \in R^3)$

(c) $\phi : (x_1, x_2, x_3) \longmapsto \pi x_1$ $\quad ((x_1, x_2, x_3) \in R^3)$

(d) $\phi : (x_1, x_2, x_3) \longmapsto x_1 + 1$ $\quad ((x_1, x_2, x_3) \in R^3)$

(e) $\phi : x \longmapsto (x, x, x)$ $\quad (x \in R)$

(f) $\phi : x \longmapsto 2x$ $\quad (x \in R)$

(g) $\phi : (x_1, x_2) \longmapsto \sqrt{2}\,(x_2 - 3x_1)$ $\quad ((x_1, x_2) \in R^2)$

(ii) Write down the matrix representations, in the standard bases, of those of the above functions which are linear functionals.

2. Is there always a natural isomorphism of U onto $\hat{U}$:

(i) if U is finite-dimensional?
(ii) if U is infinite-dimensional?

3. Is there always a natural isomorphism of U onto $\hat{\hat{U}}$:

(i) if U is finite-dimensional?
(ii) if U is infinite-dimensional?

4. Complete the following:

If $\{\alpha_1, \ldots, \alpha_n\}$ is a basis for U and $\{\phi_1, \ldots, \phi_n\}$ is the dual basis for $\hat{U}$ then

$$\phi_i(\alpha_j) = \underline{\hspace{5cm}} \quad (i, j = 1, \ldots, n)$$

5. $\{(1, 0, 0), (1, 1, 0), (1, 1, 2)\}$ is a basis for R^3; calculate the dual basis in $\hat{R}^3$.

6. Calculate a basis for the annihilator in $\hat{R}^4$ of $\langle (1, 2, 3, 4), (4, 3, 2, 1) \rangle$.

7. $\{\alpha_1, \alpha_2, \alpha_3\}$ and $\{\alpha_1, \alpha_2, \alpha_3'\}$ are two bases of R^3; differing only in the third basis element, and if $\{\phi_1, \phi_2, \phi_3\}$ and $\{\phi_1', \phi_2', \phi_3'\}$ are the corresponding dual bases, use the concept of an annihilator to prove that ϕ_3' is a scalar multiple of ϕ_3.

8. A mathematically-minded landowner decides to start up a "game-park" on his land, and wishes to calculate how many antelopes of various sorts his land can take. He consults

(a) a book which tells how much land per animal various different species of antelope require;

(b) a map of his land, to calculate how many acres he has at his disposal;

(c) an employment agency, to tell him how many men are available to work on the project.

He then calculates:

(d) a suitable population of antelopes for his game-park.

Which of the quantities measured by (a), (b) and (c) can be said to be in the "dual space" corresponding to quantity measured by (d)?

Solutions to Self-assessment Test

1. (i) The mappings in (b), (c), (f) and (g) are linear functionals. The mappings (a) and (e) are not because their codomains are not R, and the mapping (d) is not because $\phi(0) \neq 0$.

   (ii) (b) $[2 \ \ 3 \ \ 0]$
   (c) $[\pi \ \ 0 \ \ 0]$
   (f) $[2]$
   (g) $[-3\sqrt{2} \ \ \sqrt{2} \ \ 0]$

2. (i) No
   (ii) No

3. (i) Yes, the natural isomorphism: $\alpha \longmapsto \tilde{\alpha}$.
   (ii) No

4. δ_{ij}

5. We must invert $\begin{bmatrix} 1 & 1 & 1 \\ 0 & 1 & 1 \\ 0 & 0 & 2 \end{bmatrix}$ and read off the rows. This gives

   $\{[1 \ \ -1 \ \ 0], [0 \ \ 1 \ \ -\frac{1}{2}], [0 \ \ 0 \ \ \frac{1}{2}]\}$ as the basis.

6. The annihilator is the set of all $[a \ b \ c \ d]$ such that

   $$a + 2b + 3c + 4d = 0,$$
   $$4a + 3b + 2c + d = 0.$$

   Bringing the coefficient matrix to Hermite normal form, an equivalent system is

   $$a - c - 2d = 0,$$
   $$b + 2c + 3d = 0.$$

   Thus an arbitrary element of the annihilator is

   $$c[1 \ \ -2 \ \ 1 \ \ 0] + d[2 \ \ -3 \ \ 0 \ \ 1],$$

   so a basis is

   $$\{[1 \ \ -2 \ \ 1 \ \ 0], [2 \ \ -3 \ \ 0 \ \ 1]\}.$$

7. The annihilator of $\langle \alpha_1, \alpha_2 \rangle$ is one-dimensional. By the properties of dual bases,

   $$\phi_3(\alpha_1) = 0 = \phi_3(\alpha_2),$$

   and

   $$\phi_3'(\alpha_1) = 0 = \phi_3'(\alpha_2).$$

   Thus, both ϕ_3 and ϕ_3' are in $\langle \alpha_1, \alpha_2 \rangle^\perp$, and they must therefore be scalar multiples of one another.

8. The best answer is (a), since if he has (say) g gnus, h hartebeest, i impalas and k kudu on his land, and if a gnu requires G acres, a hartebeest H acres, an impala I acres and a kudu K acres, then the total amount of land he must have in order for them to live healthily is

   $$[G \ H \ I \ K]\begin{bmatrix} g \\ h \\ i \\ k \end{bmatrix} \text{ acres.}$$

Unit 13   Systems of Differential Equations

Contents

Set Books

D. L. Kreider, R. G. Kuller, D. R. Ostberg and F. W. Perkins, *An Introduction to Linear Analysis* (Addison-Wesley, 1966).

E. D. Nering, *Linear Algebra and Matrix Theory* (John Wiley, 1970).

It is essential to have these books; the course is based on them and will not make sense without them.

This unit is based on a reprint, which is contained in the flap inside the back cover of this text. The reprint is taken from:
D. L. Kreider, R. G. Kuller and D. R. Ostberg, *Elementary Differential Equations* (Addison-Wesley, 1968).

Conventions

Before working through this correspondence text make sure you have read *A Guide to the Linear Mathematics Course*. Of the typographical conventions given in the Guide the following are the most important.

The set books are referred to as:
    K for *An Introduction to Linear Analysis*
    N for *Linear Algebra and Matrix Theory*
The reprint is referred to as **S**.

All starred items in the summaries are examinable.

References to the Open University Mathematics Foundation Course Units (The Open University Press, 1971) take the form *Unit M100 3, Operations and Morphisms*.

13.0   Introduction

We have discussed on several occasions the representation of an electrical network by a differential equation using Kirchhoff's Laws.

constant current source

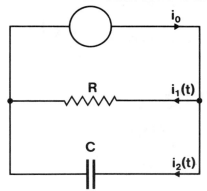

For example, the network shown in the diagram is mentioned in *Unit 4, Differential Equations I* (Exercise 3, sub-section 4.2); it is described by a *system of equations*

$$R\frac{di_1}{dt} - C\frac{dq_2}{dt} = 0$$

$$i_1(t) + i_2(t) = i_0 \qquad (t \in R_0^+)$$

$$i_2(t) = \frac{dq_2}{dt}$$

We could solve these equations by eliminating all but one of the unknown functions to obtain a single differential equation. In this unit we adopt a different approach which allows us to solve *directly* such a system of differential equations.

The unit is divided into three sections. In the first section we describe what we mean by a system of differential equations, and having done that we use the analogy with a single linear differential equation to say what it means to find a solution and to consider the existence of solutions. We also show how a single differential equation can be considered as a first order system of differential equations. In the second section we shall look at constant-coefficient homogeneous systems and use the methods of eigenvectors, eigenvalues and Jordan normal form to solve such systems. The final section deals with physical applications.

This unit covers most of the material from a supplement.* This material on systems of linear differential equations by the authors Kreider, Kuller and Ostberg is written in the same style as **K**. If you are happy with this style, you may wish to read more on the subject than just the selection we treat in this unit. You will also find a discussion in Section VI.7 of **N**.

We use the symbol **S** to refer to the Supplement, which is contained in the flap inside the back cover of this text.

---

* This material is taken from: D. L. Kreider, R. G. Kuller and D. R. Ostberg, *Elementary Differential Equations* (Addison-Wesley, 1968).

13.1 SYSTEMS OF DIFFERENTIAL EQUATIONS

13.1.1 A New Linear Operator

READ Section 5–6 pages S224–225.

Notes

(i) *line 12, page* S224 "in the preceding section". This corresponds to the discussion of linear problems in *Unit 3, Hermite Normal Form* (pages N63–64).

(ii) *Equation (5-21), page* S224 This equation is not an application of matrix multiplication but a *definition* of how L operates on a column matrix $\mathbf{X}$. The usual interpretation of a matrix as *representing* a linear transformation is not valid because the elements L_{ij} are differential operators, and these do not form a field (e.g. D has no multiplicative inverse over $\mathcal{C}^\infty[a, b]$).

(iii) *line −15, page* S225 "operator equations". This is another expression for "linear problems" (see page **K80**).

Exercise

Exercise 2, page S225.

Solution

Let $\mathbf{X}_1$ and $\mathbf{X}_2$ be two vectors in $\mathcal{V}_n$, λ_1, $\lambda_2 \in R$. Then if
$\mathbf{X}_i = (x_{1i}, \ldots, x_{ni})$,

$$L(\lambda_1 \mathbf{X}_1 + \lambda_2 \mathbf{X}_2)$$

$$= \begin{bmatrix} L_{11} & \cdots & L_{1n} \\ \vdots & & \vdots \\ L_{m1} & \cdots & L_{mn} \end{bmatrix} \begin{bmatrix} \lambda_1 x_{11} + \lambda_2 x_{12} \\ \vdots \\ \lambda_1 x_{n1} + \lambda_2 x_{n2} \end{bmatrix}$$

$$= \begin{bmatrix} L_{11}(\lambda_1 x_{11} + \lambda_2 x_{12}) + \cdots + L_{1n}(\lambda_1 x_{n1} + \lambda_2 x_{n2}) \\ \vdots \\ L_{m1}(\lambda_1 x_{11} + \lambda_2 x_{12}) + \cdots + L_{mn}(\lambda_1 x_{n1} + \lambda_2 x_{n2}) \end{bmatrix}$$

$$= \lambda_1 \begin{bmatrix} L_{11}x_{11} + \cdots + L_{1n}x_{n1} \\ \vdots \\ L_{m1}x_{11} + \cdots + L_{mn}x_{n1} \end{bmatrix}$$

$$+ \lambda_2 \begin{bmatrix} L_{11}x_{12} + \cdots + L_{1n}x_{n2} \\ \vdots \\ L_{m1}x_{12} + \cdots + L_{mn}x_{n2} \end{bmatrix}$$

$$= \lambda_1 L\mathbf{X}_1 + \lambda_2 L\mathbf{X}_2.$$

13.1.2 Normal First-order Systems

If we want to solve some systems of equations we have to restrict the type of system that we shall be looking at. We shall restrict ourselves to first-order systems from now on. In fact, we shall find that this is not as serious a restriction as it seems, because a lot of systems can be reduced to first order systems.

READ Section 5–7 from page S225 *to the end of page* S227.

Notes

(i) *line* -4 *to the end of page* S225. For example, the system (written in terms of functions and derived functions)

$$(D+1)x_1 + Dx_2 = h_1$$
$$(D-1)x_1 - x_2 = h_2$$

is of first order. This is the same as

$$Dx_1 + Dx_2 = -x_1 + h_1$$
$$Dx_1 \qquad = x_1 + x_2 + h_2$$

Solving for Dx_1 and Dx_2, we get

$$Dx_1 = x_1 + x_2 + h_2$$
$$Dx_2 = -2x_1 - x_2 + h_1 - h_2.$$

We can usually rearrange a first-order system where the number of equations is the same as the number of unknowns in precisely this way into the *normal form*.

(ii) *line 1, page* S227 "functional n-space" means $\mathcal{V}_n$.

(iii) *line 8, page* S227 What is meant here is that $\mathbf{X}_0 \in \mathcal{R}^n$ is the n-tuple of images of t_0 under the functions $x_1, \ldots, x_n$.

(iv) *line* -1, *page* S227 Chapter 2 here corresponds to Chapter 3 of **K**.

Exercises

1. Exercise 1, page S231
2. Exercise 2, page S231.
3. Put the following system of equations into normal form.

$$Dx_1(t) + x_2(t) + Dx_3(t) = e^t$$
$$x_1(t) + x_2(t) + Dx_3(t) = 0$$
$$Dx_2(t) + 2x_3(t) = \sin t.$$

Solutions

1. (a) First write out the system in terms of equations to get

$$x_1'(t) = x_2(t), \; x_2'(t) = x_3(t),$$
$$x_3'(t) = 2x_1(t) + x_2(t) - 3x_3(t) + e^t.$$

Now use the first two equations to write everything in terms of $x_1(t)$ and its derivatives.

$$x_1'''(t) = 2x_1(t) + x_1'(t) - 3x_1''(t) + e^t$$

Rearranging and writing x for x_1

$$x'''(t) + 3x''(t) - x'(t) - 2x(t) = e^t.$$

(b) In a similar way to that in (a) we obtain

$$x''(t) - q(t)x'(t) - p(t)x(t) = f(t).$$

2. Follow the procedure on page S226.

(a)
$$\begin{bmatrix} x_1'(t) \\ x_2'(t) \\ x_3'(t) \end{bmatrix} = \begin{bmatrix} 0 & 1 & 0 \\ 0 & 0 & 1 \\ -e^t & 0 & -\cos t \end{bmatrix} \begin{bmatrix} x_1(t) \\ x_2(t) \\ x_3(t) \end{bmatrix} + \begin{bmatrix} 0 \\ 0 \\ t^2 + 1 \end{bmatrix}$$

(b)
$$\begin{bmatrix} x_1'(t) \\ x_2'(t) \\ x_3'(t) \\ x_4'(t) \end{bmatrix} = \begin{bmatrix} 0 & 1 & 0 & 0 \\ 0 & 0 & 1 & 0 \\ 0 & 0 & 0 & 1 \\ 0 & 0 & -e^t & 0 \end{bmatrix} \begin{bmatrix} x_1(t) \\ x_2(t) \\ x_3(t) \\ x_4(t) \end{bmatrix} + \begin{bmatrix} 0 \\ 0 \\ 0 \\ \cos t \end{bmatrix}$$

3. Use the procedure in note (i) to the reading passage. Solve for the derivatives.

$$Dx_1(t) = x_1(t) \qquad\qquad\qquad + e^t$$
$$Dx_2(t) = \qquad\qquad -2x_3(t) + \sin t$$
$$Dx_3(t) = -x_1(t) - x_2(t)$$

so that

$$\begin{bmatrix} Dx_1(t) \\ Dx_2(t) \\ Dx_3(t) \end{bmatrix} = \begin{bmatrix} 1 & 0 & 0 \\ 0 & 0 & -2 \\ -1 & -1 & 0 \end{bmatrix} \begin{bmatrix} x_1(t) \\ x_2(t) \\ x_3(t) \end{bmatrix} + \begin{bmatrix} e^t \\ \sin t \\ 0 \end{bmatrix}$$

13.1.3   The Solution Space

We turn now to the problem of trying to solve a system of linear differential equations. We proceed much as we did in *Unit 9, Differential Equations II*, where we discussed ordinary differential equations.

Before solving specific systems, we first look to see if there are in fact solutions to be found and, if so, how many. In other words, do we have an existence and uniqueness theorem (page **K**104)? And what is the dimension on the solution space (page **K**106)?

*READ from the top of page S228 to the end of the statement of **Lemma 5-1**, and then the statement of **Theorem 5-12** on page S229.*

Notes

(i)   *line 4, page S228* If we let D be the differentiation operator from $\mathcal{V}_n$ to $\mathcal{V}_n$

$$D : X \longmapsto X'$$

then $X' = AX$ is equivalent to $(D - A)X = 0$. Thus the solution set is the kernel of the linear operator $D - A$ acting on $\mathcal{V}_n$.

(ii)   *Theorem 5-11, page S228* This theorem can be stated in another way using an idea from *Unit 9*. Let $\mathcal{W}$ be the solution set of the system of equations considered, and let E denote the function from $\mathcal{W}$ to $\mathcal{R}^n$ defined by

$$E : X \longmapsto X(t_0).$$

Then the theorem states that E is one-to-one (since the X for a given X_0 is unique) and onto (since this X exists for all X_0). In the homogeneous case $\mathcal{W}$ is a subspace and E is a linear transformation, so that it is a (vector space) isomorphism. We call it the *initial condition isomorphism*.

(iii)   *line 17, page S228* Chapter 2 corresponds to Chapter 3 of **K**. Chapter 9 material is covered in *Unit 33, Existence and Uniqueness Theorem for Differential Equations*.

(iv)   *Lemma 5-1, page S228* $X_1(t_0), \ldots, X_k(t_0)$ are vectors in $\mathcal{R}^n$ since each X_i is an n-tuple of functions and each $X_i(t_0)$ is the n-tuple of values of these functions at t_0. This lemma follows directly from the existence of the initial condition isomorphism.

(v)   *Theorem 5-12, page S229* This also follows directly from the fact that E is an isomorphism. Since an nth order differential equation is equivalent to an $n \times n$ first-order system, the corresponding result for the solution space is a particular case of Theorem 5-12.

Exercise

Let

$$A = \begin{bmatrix} 0 & 2 \\ -2 & 0 \end{bmatrix} \qquad B(t) = \begin{bmatrix} \cos t \\ 2\sin t \end{bmatrix}$$

(i)   Which of the following vectors in $\mathcal{V}_2$ are solutions of $X' = AX$?

(a) $\begin{bmatrix} \cos 2t \\ \sin 2t \end{bmatrix}$
(b) $\begin{bmatrix} -\cos 2t \\ \sin 2t \end{bmatrix}$
(c) $\begin{bmatrix} \sin 2t \\ \cos 2t \end{bmatrix}$

(d) $\begin{bmatrix} 2\sin t \\ \tfrac{1}{2}\cos t \end{bmatrix}$

(ii) Show that $\mathbf{X}(t) = \begin{bmatrix} \sin t \\ 0 \end{bmatrix}$ is a solution of $\mathbf{X}' = A\mathbf{X} + \mathbf{B}$.

(iii) Find the complete solution of the system $\mathbf{X}' = A\mathbf{X} + \mathbf{B}$.

Solution

(i) We try each in turn. For example if

$$\mathbf{X}(t) = \begin{bmatrix} \cos 2t \\ \sin 2t \end{bmatrix}, \qquad \mathbf{X}'(t) = -\begin{bmatrix} 2 \sin 2t \\ 2 \cos 2t \end{bmatrix}$$

$$= 2\begin{bmatrix} -\sin 2t \\ \cos 2t \end{bmatrix}$$

$$A\mathbf{X}(t) = \begin{bmatrix} 0 & 2 \\ -2 & 0 \end{bmatrix}\begin{bmatrix} \cos 2t \\ \sin 2t \end{bmatrix} = \begin{bmatrix} 2 \sin 2t \\ -2 \cos 2t \end{bmatrix}$$

$$= 2\begin{bmatrix} \sin 2t \\ -\cos 2t \end{bmatrix}$$

Thus $\mathbf{X}' \neq A\mathbf{X}$, and so this $\mathbf{X}(t)$ is not a solution. Similarly, (b) and (c) are solutions; (d) is not.

(ii) $\mathbf{X}'(t) = \begin{bmatrix} \cos t \\ 0 \end{bmatrix}$, and $A\mathbf{X}(t) = \begin{bmatrix} 0 & 2 \\ -2 & 0 \end{bmatrix}\begin{bmatrix} \sin t \\ 0 \end{bmatrix} = \begin{bmatrix} 0 \\ -2 \sin t \end{bmatrix}$

Therefore

$$A\mathbf{X}(t) + \mathbf{B}(t) = \begin{bmatrix} 0 \\ -2 \sin t \end{bmatrix} + \begin{bmatrix} \cos t \\ 2 \sin t \end{bmatrix} = \begin{bmatrix} \cos t \\ 0 \end{bmatrix}$$

Hence, $\mathbf{X}' = A\mathbf{X} + \mathbf{B}$, if $\mathbf{X}(t) = \begin{bmatrix} \sin t \\ 0 \end{bmatrix}$.

(iii) We must

(a) find one particular solution

and

(b) solve $\mathbf{X}' = A\mathbf{X}$

(a) has been answered in part (ii),

$$\mathbf{X}(t) = \begin{bmatrix} \sin t \\ 0 \end{bmatrix}$$

is a particular solution.

(b) To solve $\mathbf{X}' = A\mathbf{X}$, find a basis for the solution space. Theorem 5–12 tells us that we need two basis vectors In part (i) we found two solutions for $\mathbf{X}' = A\mathbf{X}$:

$$\mathbf{X}_1(t) = \begin{bmatrix} -\cos 2t \\ \sin 2t \end{bmatrix} \qquad \mathbf{X}_2(t) = \begin{bmatrix} \sin 2t \\ \cos 2t \end{bmatrix}$$

These will form a basis for the solution space if they are linearly independent. To test for linear independence we use Lemma 5–1. Let $t_0 = 0$, then

$$\mathbf{X}_1(0) = \begin{bmatrix} -1 \\ 0 \end{bmatrix}, \qquad \mathbf{X}_2(0) = \begin{bmatrix} 0 \\ 1 \end{bmatrix}.$$

Since these vectors are linearly independent in R^2, $\mathbf{X}_1$ and $\mathbf{X}_2$ are linearly independent in $\mathcal{V}_2$.

We can now write down the complete solution. Every solution of $\mathbf{X}' = A\mathbf{X} + \mathbf{B}$ has the form

$$\mathbf{X}(t) = \lambda\begin{bmatrix} -\cos 2t \\ \sin 2t \end{bmatrix} + \mu\begin{bmatrix} \sin 2t \\ \cos 2t \end{bmatrix} + \begin{bmatrix} \sin t \\ 0 \end{bmatrix}$$

$$= \begin{bmatrix} \sin t - \lambda \cos 2t + \mu \sin 2t \\ \lambda \sin 2t + \mu \cos 2t \end{bmatrix}$$

where λ, μ are real numbers.

13.1.4 The Wronskian

The solution space of an $n \times n$ first order system of equations has dimension n, and if $\{X_1, \ldots, X_n\}$ is a basis (each X_i being an n-tuple of functions) then the general solution is $\sum_{j=1}^{n} c_j X_j$. In general, given n solutions $X_1, \ldots, X_n$, we must have some means of determining whether they are linearly independent. As we saw in the Exercise of the previous sub-section the method is to use Lemma 5-1, i.e. we choose a suitable point t_0 at which we define an initial condition isomorphism E and consider whether $EX_1, \ldots, EX_n \in R^n$ are linearly independent. This is equivalent to demanding that the determinant $D(EX_1, \ldots, EX_n) \neq 0$, for any t_0 in the interval I.

We extend this idea by defining an initial condition isomorphism E_t for each point $t \in I$. Then the real function with domain I defined by

$$t \longmapsto D(E_t X_1, \ldots, E_t X_n) = \begin{vmatrix} x_{11}(t) & \cdots & x_{1n}(t) \\ \vdots & & \vdots \\ x_{n1}(t) & \cdots & x_{nn}(t) \end{vmatrix}$$

where $X_i = (x_{1i}, \ldots, x_{ni})$, is called the *Wronskian* and is denoted by $W[X_1, \ldots, X_n]$.

READ from line -5 on page S229 to line 12 of page S230.

Notes

(i) *line 1, page S230* There is nothing unusual about the determinant. All that we are doing is expressing the matrix elements in the form of the image of a function.

(ii) *line 5, page S230* "if and only if" Both these conditions follow immediately by the isomorphism between $\mathcal{W}$ and $\mathcal{R}^n$.

(iii) *line 11, page S230* The Wronskian is defined in Section 3-6 of **K**. The system of equations which was introduced *ad hoc* in *Unit 9*, sub-section 9.2.2, is the basis of the idea.

Exercises

1. (i) Show that $X_1(t) = \begin{bmatrix} 1 \\ 2 \end{bmatrix}$ and $X_2(t) = \begin{bmatrix} -e^{3t} \\ e^{3t} \end{bmatrix}$ are solutions of

$$X' = AX \quad (t \in R),$$

where $A = \begin{bmatrix} 2 & -1 \\ -2 & 1 \end{bmatrix}$.

(ii) Determine the Wronskian of these two solutions.

(iii) Characterise the solution space of $X' = AX$ in terms of X_1 and X_2.

2. (i) Write $(D^2 - 1)x = 0$ as a normal system in matrix form.

(ii) Use the *Remark* on page S230 with the differential equation $(D^2 - 1)x = 0$ to obtain a basis for the solution space of the system you obtained in part (i).

Solutions

1. (i) $X_1(t) = \begin{bmatrix} 1 \\ 2 \end{bmatrix}$; therefore $X_1'(t) = \begin{bmatrix} 0 \\ 0 \end{bmatrix}$.

$$AX_1(t) = \begin{bmatrix} 2 & -1 \\ -2 & 1 \end{bmatrix} \begin{bmatrix} 1 \\ 2 \end{bmatrix} = \begin{bmatrix} 0 \\ 0 \end{bmatrix} = X_1'(t)$$

$$X_2(t) = \begin{bmatrix} -e^{3t} \\ e^{3t} \end{bmatrix}; \quad \text{therefore } X_2'(t) = \begin{bmatrix} -3e^{3t} \\ 3e^{3t} \end{bmatrix}$$

$$AX_2(t) = \begin{bmatrix} 2 & -1 \\ -2 & 1 \end{bmatrix} \begin{bmatrix} -e^{3t} \\ e^{3t} \end{bmatrix} = \begin{bmatrix} -3e^{3t} \\ 3e^{3t} \end{bmatrix} = X_2'(t)$$

(ii) $W[\mathbf{X}_1, \mathbf{X}_2]$ is given by

$$t \longmapsto \begin{vmatrix} 1 & -e^{3t} \\ 2 & e^{3t} \end{vmatrix} = 3e^{3t} \neq 0 \quad (t \in R)$$

(iii)   By part (ii), $\mathbf{X}_1$ and $\mathbf{X}_2$ are linearly independent. Thus the solution space is

$$\{\mathbf{X} : \exists\, c_1, c_2 \in R \text{ such that } \mathbf{X} = c_1 \mathbf{X}_1 + c_2 \mathbf{X}_2\}.$$

2. (i) $DX = \begin{bmatrix} 0 & 1 \\ 1 & 0 \end{bmatrix} \mathbf{X}$

(ii)   The solutions of a differential equation with constant coefficients are $t \longmapsto e^{\lambda t}$ where λ satisfies the characteristic equation. In our case we require $\lambda^2 - 1 = 0$, i.e. $\lambda = \pm 1$. This gives the basis $\{e^t, e^{-t}\}$ for the solution space of $(D^2 - 1)x = 0$. The Wronskian is (see *Unit 9*)

$$W[e^t, e^{-t}] : t \longmapsto \begin{vmatrix} e^t & e^{-t} \\ e^t & -e^{-t} \end{vmatrix}$$

By the *Remark* this is the Wronskian for a basis of the solution space $\{\mathbf{X} : DX = \begin{bmatrix} 0 & 1 \\ 1 & 0 \end{bmatrix} \mathbf{X}\}$. Thus a basis is

$$\left\{ \begin{bmatrix} 1 \\ 1 \end{bmatrix} e^t, \quad \begin{bmatrix} 1 \\ -1 \end{bmatrix} e^{-t} \right\}.$$

13.1.5   Summary of Section 13.1

In this section we have defined the terms

system of linear differential equations	(page S224)
homogeneous system	(page S224)
nonhomogeneous system	(page S224)
operator matrix	(page S224)
normal first-order system	(page S225)
Wronskian	(page C10)

Theorems

1. (**Theorem 5-11**, page S228)
Let $\mathbf{X}' = A(t)\mathbf{X} + \mathbf{B}(t)$

be a normal $n \times n$-first order system of linear differential equations defined on an interval I. Then if t_0 is any point in I and $\mathbf{X}_0$ is any vector in $\mathscr{R}^n$, the given system has a unique solution $\mathbf{X} = \mathbf{X}(t)$ such that $\mathbf{X}(t_0) = \mathbf{X}_0$.

2. (**Initial Condition Isomorphism Theorem**, page C8)
Let $\mathcal{W}$ be the solution set of $\mathbf{X}'(t) = A(t)\mathbf{X}(t) + \mathbf{B}(t)$, $t \in I$, and let $E : \mathcal{W} \longrightarrow \mathscr{R}^n$ be specified by $E(\mathbf{X}) = \mathbf{X}(t_0)$, $t_0 \in I$. Then E is one-to-one and onto.

3. (**Theorem 5-12**, page S229)
The dimension of the solution space $\mathcal{W}$ of any homogeneous $n \times n$-system $\mathbf{X}' = A(t)\mathbf{X}$ is n, the number of equations in the system.

Technique

Given a system of first-order linear differential equations, put it into normal form.

Notation

$\mathbf{X}$	(page S224)
$\mathcal{V}_n$	(page S225)
E	(page C8)
E_t	(page C10)
$W[\mathbf{X}_1, \ldots, \mathbf{X}]_n$	(page C10)

13.2 CONSTANT-COEFFICIENT SYSTEMS

13.2.0 Introduction

In the preceding section we saw that a normal first-order system can be written in the form

$$(D - A)\mathbf{X} = \mathbf{B}$$

where D is the differentiation operator from $\mathcal{V}_n$ to $\mathcal{V}_n$ defined in sub-section 13.1.3. As this is a linear problem we immediately know that solving the system involves:

(i)   finding a particular solution $\mathbf{X}_p$ such that $(D - A)\mathbf{X}_p = \mathbf{B}$
(ii) finding the kernel of $(D - A)$.

As with a single differential equation there is no specific method for finding particular solutions, but we could develop a method of variation of para-meters in the manner of *Unit 11, Differential Equations III*. This method will not be dealt with in this unit, though it is described in the remainder of Section 5-7 of S. If you have the time you might like to read it.

In this section we discuss the second part of the problem: solving

$$(D - A)\mathbf{X} = \mathbf{0}.$$

We know from the previous section that solving $(D - A)\mathbf{X} = \mathbf{0}$ is pre-cisely the problem of finding a basis for an n-dimensional subspace of $\mathcal{V}_n$. ($\mathcal{V}_n$ is itself an *infinite* dimensional vector space.) As in *Unit 9*, we will find a basis for this kernel when we have a constant-coefficient system, that is when A is a matrix of constants. In this case we can apply the theory we have developed in *Units 5* and *10, Determinants and Eigenvalues* and *Jordan Normal Form*; we can diagonalize A or reduce A to Jordan normal form.

Before you proceed you should make sure that you are familiar with the definitions of *eigenvalue, eigenvector*, and *characteristic equation* treated in *Unit 5*, and that you know how to find the eigenvectors of a 3×3 matrix. An alternative method for solving constant-coefficient systems is dealt with in Section 5-8 of S. We shall not be discussing it in this text.

This section is in three parts. We first consider the simple case where A is diagonable over R. We then generalize to the case when the characteristic polynomial can be expressed in linear factors so that the Jordan normal form is a real matrix. Finally we study the case when the characteristic polynomial has irreducible factors, resulting in a periodic term as in *Unit 9*.

13.2.1   Real Eigenvalues with an Eigenvector Basis

We are considering the system $\mathbf{X}' = A\mathbf{X}$ where A is a constant matrix and we are looking for a n-tuple of functions $\mathbf{X}$ which is a solution of this system. If we had been considering a single equation $x' = ax$, then a solution would have been $x(t) = e^{at}$ and this suggests that a solution to $\mathbf{X}' = A\mathbf{X}$ might be an n-tuple of exponential functions $t \longmapsto e^{\lambda t}$, where the scalars λ somehow characterize the matrix A.

READ Section 5-11 on page S250 *to line* -11 *on page* S252.

Notes

(i)   *Lemma 5-3, page* S251 Because A is a matrix of constants we can calculate eigenvalues and eigenvectors for A. The n-tuple of functions $\mathbf{X}_\lambda$ is the n-tuple

$$\mathbf{X}_\lambda(t) = \begin{bmatrix} e_1 e^{\lambda t} \\ e_2 e^{\lambda t} \\ \vdots \\ e_n e^{\lambda t} \end{bmatrix} = e^{\lambda t} \mathbf{E}_\lambda$$

(ii)   *line 10, page* S251 This line follows since $\mathbf{X}_\lambda = \mathbf{E}_\lambda e^{\lambda t}$.
(iii)   *line 14, page* S251 Here we could have used Lemma 5-1 on page S228 with $t_0 = 0$.
(iv)   *line 17, page* S251 Eigenvectors for distinct eigenvalues are linearly independent, as we saw in *Unit 5* (page K463, Theorem 12-1).

Exercise

Solve the system of equations

$$Dx_1 = 5x_1 + 4x_2$$
$$Dx_2 = -x_1.$$

Solution

The system may be written in matrix form as $\mathbf{X}' = A\mathbf{X}$ with

$$A = \begin{bmatrix} 5 & 4 \\ -1 & 0 \end{bmatrix}.$$

$|A - \lambda I| = \lambda^2 - 5\lambda + 4 = (\lambda - 1)(\lambda - 4).$

Let $\mathbf{E}_1 = (e_1, e_2)^*$ be an eigenvector corresponding to the eigenvalue 1. Then

$$\begin{bmatrix} 4 & 4 \\ -1 & -1 \end{bmatrix} \begin{bmatrix} e_1 \\ e_2 \end{bmatrix} = \begin{bmatrix} 0 \\ 0 \end{bmatrix}$$

and a solution is $e_1 = 1$, $e_2 = -1$.

i.e. $\mathbf{E}_1 = (1, -1)$.

Similarly $(A - 4)\mathbf{E}_4 = \mathbf{0}$

$$\begin{bmatrix} 1 & 4 \\ -1 & -4 \end{bmatrix} \begin{bmatrix} e_3 \\ e_4 \end{bmatrix} = \begin{bmatrix} 0 \\ 0 \end{bmatrix}$$

which has a solution

$\mathbf{E}_4 = (4, -1)$

Hence using Lemma 5-3 the general solution is

$$c_1 \mathbf{E}_1 e^t + c_2 \mathbf{E}_4 e^{4t}, \ (c_1, c_2 \in R).$$

i.e. $\{\mathbf{E}_1 e^t, \mathbf{E}_4 e^{4t}\}$ form a basis for the solution space.

The method described in the reading passage and the exercise allows us to solve the matrix equation $\mathbf{X}' = A\mathbf{X}$ when the $n \times n$ matrix A has n distinct eigenvalues. The object of requiring n distinct eigenvalues was to ensure n

---

* Recall that 1-column matrices can be written $(a_1, a_2, \ldots, a_n)$.

linearly independent eigenvectors in R^n, which by Lemma 5-1 would yield n linearly independent eigenvectors in $\mho_n$ which form a basis for the solution space. In fact we know that it is possible to have an eigenvector basis for R^n even when there are less than n distinct eigenvalues, in which case the theory of this sub-section remains valid.

Theorem

If the eigenvectors $\mathbf{E}_1, \ldots, \mathbf{E}_n$ of an $n \times n$ matrix A form a basis for R^n, then the general solution of $\mathbf{X}' = A\mathbf{X}$ is

$$\mathbf{X}(t) = c_1\mathbf{E}_1 e^{\lambda_1 t} + \cdots + c_n\mathbf{E}_n e^{\lambda_n t}$$

where $\mathbf{E}_i$ is an eigenvector corresponding to λ_i.

Example

To solve $\mathbf{X}' = A\mathbf{X}$ where

$$A = \begin{bmatrix} 4 & -1 & -1 \\ 1 & 2 & -1 \\ 1 & -1 & 2 \end{bmatrix}$$

we first find the eigenvalues of A.

The characteristic polynomial of A is, as you can check, $|A - \lambda I| = -(\lambda - 3)^2(\lambda - 2)$. The eigenvalues satisfy $|A - \lambda I| = 0$, i.e. $\lambda = 2$, $\lambda = 3$. The eigenvector $\mathbf{E}_2 = (e_1, e_2, e_3)$ corresponding to the eigenvalue 2 must satisfy

$$(A - 2I)\mathbf{E}_2 = 0 \text{ i.e. } \begin{bmatrix} 2 & -1 & -1 \\ 1 & 0 & -1 \\ 1 & -1 & 0 \end{bmatrix}\begin{bmatrix} e_1 \\ e_2 \\ e_3 \end{bmatrix} = \begin{bmatrix} 0 \\ 0 \\ 0 \end{bmatrix}$$

A suitable choice is $\mathbf{E}_2 = (1, 1, 1)$. Similarly $(A - 3I)\mathbf{E}_3 = 0$ i.e.

$$\begin{bmatrix} 1 & -1 & -1 \\ 1 & -1 & -1 \\ 1 & -1 & -1 \end{bmatrix}\begin{bmatrix} e_1 \\ e_2 \\ e_3 \end{bmatrix} = \begin{bmatrix} 0 \\ 0 \\ 0 \end{bmatrix}$$

The solution space of this equation is two-dimensional and we can choose the basis $\{\mathbf{E}_3^{(1)}, \mathbf{E}_3^{(2)}\}$ where

$$\mathbf{E}_3^{(1)} = (1, 1, 0) \quad \text{and} \quad \mathbf{E}_3^{(2)} = (1, 0, 1).$$

We now have the basis $\{\mathbf{E}_2, \mathbf{E}_3^{(1)}, \mathbf{E}_3^{(2)}\}$ for R^3 and the general solution of $\mathbf{X}' = A\mathbf{X}$ is

$$c_1\mathbf{E}_2 e^{2t} + (c_2 \mathbf{E}_3^{(1)} + c_3 \mathbf{E}_3^{(2)})e^{3t}$$
$$= (c_1 e^{2t} + (c_2 + c_3)e^{3t}, c_1 e^{2t} + c_2 e^{3t}, c_1 e^{2t} + c_3 e^{3t}).$$

Exercise

Find a basis for the solution space of the system

$$\begin{aligned} x_1' &= 5x_1 - 6x_2 - 6x_3 \\ x_2' &= -x_1 + 4x_2 + 2x_3 \\ x_3' &= 3x_1 - 6x_2 - 4x_3 \end{aligned}$$

(*Hint:* $\begin{vmatrix} 5 - \lambda & -6 & -6 \\ -1 & 4 - \lambda & 2 \\ 3 & -6 & -4 - \lambda \end{vmatrix} = -(\lambda - 1)(\lambda - 2)^2$.)

Solution

If $\mathbf{X} = \begin{bmatrix} x_1 \\ x_2 \\ x_3 \end{bmatrix}$, we can write the system in the form $\mathbf{X}' = A\mathbf{X}$ with

$$A = \begin{bmatrix} 5 & -6 & -6 \\ -1 & 4 & 2 \\ 3 & -6 & -4 \end{bmatrix}$$

We proceed precisely as we did in the text and calculate the eigenvalues of A. The characteristic equation is det $(A - \lambda I) = 0$, i.e.,

$$(\lambda - 1)(\lambda - 2)^2 = 0,$$

using the hint. The eigenvalues are 1 and 2. We now calculate the eigenvectors.

For $\lambda = 1$: $(A - I)\begin{bmatrix} a_1 \\ a_2 \\ a_3 \end{bmatrix} = \begin{bmatrix} 4 & -6 & -6 \\ -1 & 3 & 2 \\ 3 & -6 & -5 \end{bmatrix} \begin{bmatrix} a_1 \\ a_2 \\ a_3 \end{bmatrix} = \begin{bmatrix} 0 \\ 0 \\ 0 \end{bmatrix}$

and we can take $\mathbf{E}_1 = (3, -1, 3)$.

For $\lambda = 2$: $(A - 2I)\begin{bmatrix} b_1 \\ b_2 \\ b_3 \end{bmatrix} = \begin{bmatrix} 3 & -6 & -6 \\ -1 & 2 & 2 \\ 3 & -6 & -6 \end{bmatrix} \begin{bmatrix} b_1 \\ b_2 \\ b_3 \end{bmatrix} = \begin{bmatrix} 0 \\ 0 \\ 0 \end{bmatrix}$

There are two linearly independent eigenvectors $\mathbf{E}_2^{(1)} = (2, 1, 0)$ and $\mathbf{E}_2^{(2)} = (2, 0, 1)$, so that $\mathbf{X}_1(t) = (3e^t, -e^t, 3e^t)$, $\mathbf{X}_2^{(1)}(t) = (2e^{2t}, e^{2t}, 0)$, $\mathbf{X}_2^{(2)}(t) = (2e^{2t}, 0, e^{2t})$ form a basis for the solution space.

13.2.2 Real Eigenvalues with no Eigenvector Basis

What we have done in the last sub-section appears to have a very *ad hoc* flavour about it. We have looked at the system $\mathbf{X}' = A\mathbf{X}$ and we have seen that if A has an eigenvector basis then we can write down the general solution of our system. Now we know that not every matrix A has an eigenvector basis (*Unit 10*). In this sub-section we will look at what we have done so far in a new light so that we can deal with the case where the characteristic polynomial of A can be written as a product of (real) linear factors, even if A does not have an eigenvector basis.

First of all then, can we look at what we have done in the previous sub-section from a different point of view? There A is diagonable; that is, there is a matrix P such that $P^{-1}AP$ is a diagonal matrix with the eigenvalues of A down the main diagonal. P, the matrix of transition, is a matrix whose columns are eigenvectors of A (*Unit 10*, Section 2). Can we exploit this to solve our systems of equations? We can. If $\mathbf{X}' = A\mathbf{X}$ is our system and S any non-singular matrix then we rewrite our system in the form

$$\mathbf{X}' = SS^{-1}ASS^{-1}\mathbf{X}$$

and interpret S as an endomorphism of $\mho_n$ writing

$$(S^{-1}\mathbf{X})' = S^{-1}AS(S^{-1}\mathbf{X}).$$

Finally putting $\mathbf{Y}$ as the image of $\mathbf{X}$ under S^{-1}, i.e., $\mathbf{Y} = S^{-1}\mathbf{X}$, we find

$$\mathbf{Y}' = (S^{-1}AS)\mathbf{Y}.$$

So we have reduced the system $\mathbf{X}' = A\mathbf{X}$ to another system $\mathbf{Y}' = (S^{-1}AS)\mathbf{Y}$. Now note that if $\mathbf{X}$ is a solution of the first system then $S^{-1}\mathbf{X}$ is a solution of the second, and conversely if $\mathbf{Y}$ is a solution of the second then $S\mathbf{Y}$ is a solution of the first. That is, we have equivalent systems. To solve the system $\mathbf{X}' = A\mathbf{X}$, we can solve $\mathbf{Y}' = (S^{-1}AS)\mathbf{Y}$, and the solution of $\mathbf{X}' = A\mathbf{X}$ is $\mathbf{X} = S\mathbf{Y}$.

This is what we have been doing in the preceding sub-section, where S was the matrix of transition which made $S^{-1}AS$ diagonal. In practice, rather than evaluate the transition matrix P and then compute the result $\mathbf{X} = P\mathbf{Y}$, it is usually more straightforward to proceed "by hand".

Example

We reconsider Example 1 on page S251. Here

$$A = \begin{bmatrix} 1 & 3 \\ 1 & -1 \end{bmatrix}$$

and an eigenvector basis is

$$\mathbf{E}_2 = (3, 1) \quad \text{and} \quad \mathbf{E}_{-2} = (-1, 1).$$

For each $t \in I$, $\mathbf{X}(t)$ is a vector in R^n so that

$$\mathbf{X}(t) = y_1(t)\mathbf{E}_2 + y_2(t)\mathbf{E}_{-2}.$$

In this way we define two real-valued functions y_1, y_2 by

$$y_i: t \longmapsto y_i(t).$$

Using this expansion in the matrix equation

$$\mathbf{X}' = A\mathbf{X}$$

we obtain

$$y_1'(t)\mathbf{E}_2 + y_2'(t)\mathbf{E}_{-2} = y_1(t)A\mathbf{E}_2 + y_2(t)A\mathbf{E}_{-2}$$
$$= 2y_1(t)\mathbf{E}_2 - 2y_2(t)\mathbf{E}_{-2}.$$

This is the equivalent system $\mathbf{Y}' = (P^{-1}AP)\mathbf{Y}$. But $\mathbf{E}_2$ and $\mathbf{E}_{-2}$ are linearly independent in R^2, so that

$$y_1'(t) = 2y_1(t)$$
$$y_2'(t) = -2y_2(t)$$

with general solutions

$$y_1(t) = c_1 e^{2t}, \qquad y_2(t) = c_2 e^{-2t}.$$

Thus

$$\mathbf{X}(t) = c_1 e^{2t}\mathbf{E}_2 + c_2 e^{-2t}\mathbf{E}_{-2}.$$

This is the solution found on page S252.

Doing the example this way is longer than applying Lemma 5-3 on page S251, because we need the eigenvalues and eigenvectors for A and having got these we can write down the solutions immediately using Lemma 5-3. But the advantage of this method is that it is constructive so that we can use it for those cases where A is *not* diagonable. We illustrate how it works in the next example.

Example

Solve the system $\mathbf{X}' = A\mathbf{X}$, where

$$A = \begin{bmatrix} 1 & 1 & 0 \\ -1 & 3 & 0 \\ -1 & 4 & -1 \end{bmatrix}$$

We saw in sub-section 10.3.2 that A does *not* have an eigenvector basis. However, its Jordan basis is $\{\mathbf{E}_1, \mathbf{E}_2, \mathbf{E}_2^I\}$ where

$$\mathbf{E}_1 = (0, 0, 1) \qquad A\mathbf{E}_1 = -\mathbf{E}_1$$
$$\mathbf{E}_2 = (1, 1, 1) \qquad A\mathbf{E}_2 = 2\mathbf{E}_2$$
$$\mathbf{E}_2^I = (-1, 0, 0) \qquad A\mathbf{E}_2^I = 2\mathbf{E}_2^I + \mathbf{E}_2$$

and hence the matrix

$$P = \begin{bmatrix} 0 & 1 & -1 \\ 0 & 1 & 0 \\ 1 & 1 & 0 \end{bmatrix}$$

is a matrix of transition such that $P^{-1}AP$ is in Jordan normal form.

$$P^{-1}AP = \begin{bmatrix} -1 & 0 & 0 \\ 0 & 2 & 1 \\ 0 & 0 & 2 \end{bmatrix}$$

So we consider the equivalent system

$$\mathbf{Y}' = (P^{-1}AP)\mathbf{Y},$$

where, as in the previous example $\mathbf{Y} = (y_1, y_2, y_3)$ and

$$\mathbf{X} = P\mathbf{Y} = y_1\mathbf{E}_1 + y_2\mathbf{E}_2 + y_3\mathbf{E}_2^{(I)}.$$

This may be written as

$$y_1' = -y_1$$
$$y_2' = 2y_2 + y_3$$
$$y_3' = 2y_3.$$

Solving this system, we find $y_1(t) = c_1 e^{-t}$, $y_3(t) = c_3 e^{2t}$ and y_2 satisfies

$$y_2'(t) = 2y_2(t) + c_3 e^{2t}.$$

Using the integrating factor method (*Unit 4*) we find that

$$y_2(t) = c_3 te^{2t} + c_2 e^{2t}.$$

We now have that

$$\begin{aligned} \mathbf{X}(t) &= P\mathbf{Y}(t) \\ &= y_1(t)\mathbf{E}_1 + y_2(t)\mathbf{E}_2 + y_3(t)\mathbf{E}_2^I \\ &= c_1\mathbf{E}_1 e^{-t} + c_2\mathbf{E}_2 e^{2t} + c_3(\mathbf{E}_2 te^{2t} + \mathbf{E}_2^I e^{2t}) \end{aligned}$$

is the general solution.

In general, when faced with a system $\mathbf{X}' = A\mathbf{X}$, we first find the Jordan basis for A. If this is possible over the reals we have obtained a real matrix P such that $J = P^{-1}AP$ is in Jordan normal form. It is then a simple matter to solve $\mathbf{Y}' = J\mathbf{Y}$, and having found its general solution, we know that $\mathbf{X} = P\mathbf{Y}$ is the general solution of $\mathbf{X}' = A\mathbf{X}$.

Exercise

Find the general solution of $\mathbf{X}' = A\mathbf{X}$ where

$$A = \begin{bmatrix} 1 & 3 & -2 \\ 0 & 7 & -4 \\ 0 & 9 & -5 \end{bmatrix}$$

(*Hint*: A Jordan normal form of A is

$$\begin{bmatrix} 1 & 1 & 0 \\ 0 & 1 & 0 \\ 0 & 0 & 1 \end{bmatrix}$$

with matrix of transition

$$\begin{bmatrix} 3 & 0 & 1 \\ 6 & 1 & 0 \\ 9 & 0 & 0 \end{bmatrix}$$

(See *Unit 10*, sub-section 10.3.3).)

Solution

We follow the procedure of this sub-section. We solve the auxiliary system

$$\mathbf{Y}' = \begin{bmatrix} 1 & 1 & 0 \\ 0 & 1 & 0 \\ 0 & 0 & 1 \end{bmatrix}\mathbf{Y}$$

that is:

$$y_1' = y_1 + y_2$$
$$y_2' = y_2$$
$$y_3' = y_3.$$

The general solutions are

$$y_3(t) = c_3 e^t, \quad y_2(t) = c_2 e^t, \quad y_1(t) = c_2 t e^t + c_1 e^t.$$

$\mathbf{X}' = A\mathbf{X}$ has the general solution

$$\mathbf{X} = P\mathbf{Y}$$
$$= (3, 6, 9)y_1 + (0, 1, 0)y_2 + (1, 0, 0)y_3$$
$$= c_1[(3, 6, 9)e^t] + c_2[(3, 6, 9)t e^t + (0, 1, 0)e^t] + c_3(1, 0, 0)e^t].$$

13.2.3   Complex Eigenvalues

In our discussion of constant-coefficient systems of differential equations $\mathbf{X}' = A\mathbf{X}$, we have so far not considered the case when A has insufficient real eigenvalues. In *Unit 10* we developed the Jordan normal form for such an A by extending our field of scalars to the complex numbers. We found that in this more general setting we could always find a matrix of transition P which reduces A to Jordan normal form, except that now P might have complex entries. We could of course still do this and consider the system $\mathbf{Y}' = (P^{-1}AP)\mathbf{Y}$, but we would have to solve equations $y_i' = \lambda y_i + y_{i+1}$ or $y_j' = \lambda y_j$, where λ may be complex.

Again there are two cases, corresponding to the existence or otherwise of an eigenvector basis. In this sub-section we consider cases where the Jordan normal form contains complex elements but is diagonal. The more general case can be treated by an extension of these ideas.

If A is an $n \times n$ matrix all of whose entries are real then Theorem 5-11 on page S228 tells us that the system $\mathbf{X}' = A\mathbf{X}$ *must* have as basis for its solution space a set of n *real* n-tuples of functions, even though A has complex eigenvalues. In fact we can find these n real-valued solution functions for the case where A has a complex eigenvector basis. In the next reading passage we see how these solutions can be found. ·

READ from line -10*, page* S252*, to line* -3*, page* S256.

Notes

(i)   The first part of this reading passage up to the end of Example 2 in page S254 covers material which should not be new to you. The vector space $\mathbb{C}^n$ was introduced in *Unit 1*, and *Unit 5* did not place any restriction on the field of scalars; so the discussion in this complex case is a revision of *Unit 5*, Section 2. The first new result is Lemma 5-4 on page S253 which relies specifically on the fact that A has real entries although it represents an endomorphism of $\mathbb{C}^n$.
(ii)   *Lemma 5-6, page* S255 If at first sight the Lemma appears complicated, read through Example 3 then return to the Lemma.
(iii)   *lines* -8 *and* -7*, page* S256 The characteristic or auxiliary equation is defined in Chapter 4 of **K**. You may recall that in a similar fashion the auxiliary equation of a recurrence relation (*Unit 7*) is the characteristic equation of the associated matrix (sub-section 5.3.2).

Exercises

1.   Exercise 1, page S257.

2.   Exercise 6(a), page S258. (The characteristic equation is $\lambda^3 + 6\lambda = 0$.)

Solutions

1. $\begin{vmatrix} -\lambda & a \\ -a & -\lambda \end{vmatrix} = \lambda^2 + a^2 = 0$

Therefore $\lambda = ia$ is one eigenvalue. Since

$$\begin{bmatrix} -ia & a \\ -a & -ia \end{bmatrix} \begin{bmatrix} x \\ y \end{bmatrix} = \begin{bmatrix} 0 \\ 0 \end{bmatrix}$$

$(1, i)$ is an eigenvector.

Using Lemma 5-6.

$$\mathbf{G}_{ia} = (1, 0), \qquad \mathbf{H}_{ia} = (0, -1).$$

Therefore

$\mathbf{X}_1(t) = (1, 0) \cos at + (0, -1) \sin at = (\cos at, -\sin at)$
$\mathbf{X}_2(t) = (0, -1) \cos at - (1, 0) \sin at = (-\sin at, -\cos at)$

The general solution is

$$\mathbf{X}(t) = \begin{bmatrix} \cos at & -\sin at \\ -\sin at & -\cos at \end{bmatrix} \begin{bmatrix} c_1 \\ c_2 \end{bmatrix}$$

$\mathbf{X}(t) \in \mathscr{R}^2.$

Let $\mathscr{R}^2$ be represented by a geometric plane and let $\mathbf{X}(t)$ be the position vector of a particle. Then, there exists $\alpha \in \mathscr{R}^+$, $\varepsilon \in (-\pi, \pi]$ such that

$c_1 = \alpha \sin \varepsilon$
$c_2 = \alpha \cos \varepsilon$

Therefore

$$\mathbf{X}(t) = (c_1 \cos at - c_2 \sin at, -c_1 \sin at - c_2 \cos at)$$
$$= \alpha(\sin(\varepsilon - at), -\cos(\varepsilon - at))$$

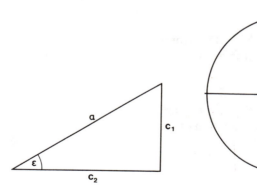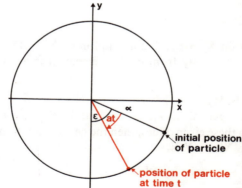

Thus the particle moves clockwise along a circular path with angular velocity a radians/unit time.

2. We have the system $\mathbf{X}' = A\mathbf{X}$, where

$$A = \begin{bmatrix} 0 & -1 & -2 \\ 1 & 0 & 1 \\ 2 & -1 & 0 \end{bmatrix}$$

We first calculate the eigenvalues for A. The characteristic equation is $\lambda^3 + 6\lambda = 0$, so that the eigenvalues are $0, +i\sqrt{6}, -i\sqrt{6}$.

We now calculate corresponding eigenvectors. Suitable choices are

$$\mathbf{E}_0 = \begin{bmatrix} 1 \\ 2 \\ -1 \end{bmatrix}, \qquad \mathbf{E}_{i\sqrt{6}} = \begin{bmatrix} 1 + 2i\sqrt{6} \\ 2 - i\sqrt{6} \\ 5 \end{bmatrix},$$

$$\mathbf{E}_{-i\sqrt{6}} = \begin{bmatrix} 1 - 2i\sqrt{6} \\ 2 + i\sqrt{6} \\ 5 \end{bmatrix}$$

Using the terminology of Lemma 5-6, we have

$$\mathbf{G}_\lambda = \begin{bmatrix} 1 \\ 2 \\ 5 \end{bmatrix} \text{ and } \mathbf{H}_\lambda = \begin{bmatrix} -2\sqrt{6} \\ \sqrt{6} \\ 0 \end{bmatrix}$$

and the general solution is

$$c_1 \begin{bmatrix} 1 \\ 2 \\ -1 \end{bmatrix} + c_2 \left(\begin{bmatrix} 1 \\ 2 \\ 5 \end{bmatrix} \cos\sqrt{6}t + \begin{bmatrix} -2 \\ 1 \\ 0 \end{bmatrix} \sqrt{6}\sin\sqrt{6}t \right)$$

$$+ c_3 \left(\begin{bmatrix} -2 \\ 1 \\ 0 \end{bmatrix} \sqrt{6}\cos\sqrt{6}t - \begin{bmatrix} 1 \\ 2 \\ 5 \end{bmatrix} \sin\sqrt{6}t \right)$$

13.2.4   Summary of Section 13.2

There were no new terms defined in this section.

Theorems

1. **(Lemma 5–3, page S251)**
For each real eigenvalue λ of A and each eigenvector

$$\mathbf{E}_\lambda = \begin{bmatrix} e_1 \\ \vdots \\ e_n \end{bmatrix}$$

belonging to λ, the function $\mathbf{X}_\lambda = \mathbf{E}_\lambda e^{\lambda t}$ is a solution of $\mathbf{X}' = A\mathbf{X}$. Moreover, solutions formed in this way from distinct eigenvalues are linearly independent in $\mathcal{V}_n$.

2. **(Corollary 5-3, page S251)**
If A has n distinct real eigenvalues $\lambda_1, \ldots, \lambda_n$ and if $\mathbf{E}_{\lambda_1}, \ldots, \mathbf{E}_{\lambda_n}$ are eigenvectors belonging to these eigenvalues, then the general solution of the normal first order system $\mathbf{X}' = A\mathbf{X}$ is

$$\mathbf{X}(t) = c_1 \mathbf{E}_{\lambda_1} e^{\lambda_1 t} + \cdots + c_n \mathbf{E}_{\lambda_n} e^{\lambda_n t},$$

where $c_1, \ldots, c_n$ are arbitrary constants.

3. **(Theorem, page C14)**
If the eigenvectors $\mathbf{E}_1, \ldots, \mathbf{E}_n$ of an $n \times n$ matrix A form a basis for R^n, then the general solution of $\mathbf{X}' = A\mathbf{X}$ is

$$\mathbf{X}(t) = c_1 \mathbf{E}_1 e^{\lambda_1 t} + \cdots + c_n \mathbf{E}_n e^{\lambda_n t}.$$

where $\mathbf{E}_i$ is an eigenvector corresponding to λ_i.

4. **(Lemma 5-4, page S253)**
Let A be an $n \times n$ matrix with real entries, and suppose that $\lambda = \alpha + \beta i$ is an eigenvalue for A. Then if $\mathbf{Z}$ is an eigenvector belonging to λ, $\overline{\mathbf{Z}}$, the complex conjugate of $\mathbf{Z}$, is an eigenvector belonging to $\overline{\lambda} = \alpha - \beta i$.

5. **(Lemma 5-5**, page S254)

Let A be a real $n \times n$-matrix, and suppose that $\mathbf{E}_\lambda$ is an eigenvector in $\mathbb{C}^n$ belonging to the complex eigenvalue $\lambda = \alpha + \beta i$ of A. Then

$$\mathbf{E}_\lambda e^{\lambda t} \quad \text{and} \quad \overline{\mathbf{E}}_\lambda e^{\bar{\lambda} t}$$

★

are solutions of the equations $\mathbf{X}' = A\mathbf{X}$.

6. **(Lemma 5-6**, page S255)

Let $\lambda = \alpha + \beta i$ be a complex eigenvalue for the $n \times n$-real matrix A, and let $\mathbf{E}_\lambda$ be an eigenvector in $\mathbb{C}^n$ belonging to λ. Then the functions

★ ★

$$\mathbf{X}_1(t) = e^{\alpha t}(\mathbf{G}_\lambda \cos \beta t + \mathbf{H}_\lambda \sin \beta t),$$

$$\mathbf{X}_2(t) = e^{\alpha t}(\mathbf{H}_\lambda \cos \beta t - \mathbf{G}_\lambda \sin \beta t)$$

where $\mathbf{G}_\lambda = \dfrac{\mathbf{E}_\lambda + \overline{\mathbf{E}}_\lambda}{2}$ and $\mathbf{H}_\lambda = \dfrac{i(\mathbf{E}_\lambda - \overline{\mathbf{E}}_\lambda)}{2}$

are linearly independent solutions of $\mathbf{X}' = A\mathbf{X}$.

Technique

Solve a normal system of equations $\mathbf{X}' = A\mathbf{X}$ were A is a matrix of real constants. The steps may be summarized in the following flow chart.

★ ★

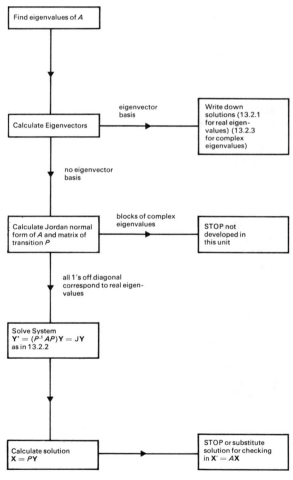

Notation

$\mathbf{E}_\lambda$	(page S251)
$\mathbf{X}_\lambda$	(page S251)
$\mathbf{E}_\lambda^{(i)}$	(page C14)
$\mathbf{G}_\lambda$	(page S255)
$\mathbf{H}_\lambda$	(page S255)

13.3   APPLICATIONS

13.3.0   Introduction

In earlier units we have seen how differential equations describe physical situations involving mechanical or electrical vibrations. In practice more than one elementary system may be linked to form a complicated one. These may be described by a system of linear differential equations, and where the coefficients are constant we may be able to solve them by the methods of Section 2. In this section we consider various physical systems and the equations which describe their behaviour.

We have seen (*Unit 4, Differential Equations I*) that a modelling situation involves three stages:

(i)   setting up the equation,
(ii)   solving the equation,
(iii)   interpreting the solution.

In this section we follow through this programme for a mechanical system and we also set up equations for electrical networks.

13.3.1   A Double Mass Spring System

The first system we shall discuss consists of two masses joined by three springs.

READ Example 1 of Section 5-12 from pages S259 *to line 10 of* S263.

Notes

(i)   *Equations* (5−51), *page* S259 The deiivation of these equations has been somewhat rushed. The most general situation has been described even though the rest of the example only considers a special situation. Two physical laws have been used. The first is Newton's law which relates the force on a particle to the acceleration of the particle. The second is Hooke's law which says that when a spring of stiffness k is extended by a distance x there is a (restoring) force kx in the opposite direction. We have two equations, one for each particle. In the first equation we have four forces acting on the mass. The first term comes from the first spring, the second term from the second spring, the fourth term from an external applied force and the third term from the viscous medium.

(ii)   *line* −5, *page* S259 The simplifying assumptions are that all three springs are identical.

(iii)   *line* 2, *page* S260 The equations (5-51) and (5-52) describe general spring systems where the end "walls" described by x_0 and x_3 can also move (as in the springing in a car). What S does here is to suppose these "walls" are fixed so that x_0 and x_3 are constant.

(iv)   *line* 11, *page* S260 "momentum variables". Here we are making a substitution, introducing new functions y_3, y_4 defined by $y_3 = m_1\dot{x}_1$, $y_4 = m_2\dot{x}_2$. It so happens that there is a physical interpretation of these functions as momentum but it is sufficient in this section to think of them as new functions. The object of the substitution is to bring the system of equations to first order.

(v)   *line* −9, *page* S261 To see that $(\mu_1 + \mu_2)^2 - 3\mu_1\mu_2 > 0$, note that $\mu_1 > 0$, $\mu_2 > 0$ and $(\mu_1 + \mu_2)^2 - 3\mu_1\mu_2 = (\mu_1 - \mu_2)^2 + \mu_1\mu_2$, which is the sum of two positive terms and so is positive. Also note that $(\mu_1 + \mu_2)^2 > (\mu_1 + \mu_2)^2 - 3\mu_1\mu_2$ so that in line −13 both values of λ^2 are negative (since $k > 0$).

(vi)   *lines* −4 *to* −1, *page* S261 This set of equations is $A\mathbf{Y} = \lambda\mathbf{Y}$.

(vii)   *line* 2, *page* S263   The equations for A_1 and A_2 are:

$$\tan A_2 = B_2/B_1, \qquad A_1 = \sqrt{B_1^2 + B_2^2}$$

This device was used in *Unit 4*, sub-section 4.4.2, and in Solution 1 of sub-section 13.2.3.

(viii)   *lines* 5–6, *page* S263 ω and ν are the *natural frequencies* of the system. The two solutions

$$(y_1(t), y_2(t)) = \left(k\cos(\omega t - A_2), \left(2k - \frac{\omega^2}{\mu_1}\right)\cos(\omega t - A_2)\right)$$

and

$$(y_1(t), y_2(t)) = \left(k \cos{(vt - A_4)}, \left(2k - \frac{v^2}{\mu_1} \right) \cos{(vt - A_4)} \right)$$

are the *normal modes of oscillation*. This particular simple behaviour arises because we set $d_1 = d_2 = 0$ and so obtained a *quadratic* in λ^2 instead of the more general quartic in λ. Thus, it would in fact have been much faster to write the system of equations (5-52) as follows:

$$m_1 \ddot{y}_1 = -2ky_1 + ky_2$$
$$m_2 \ddot{y}_2 = ky_1 - 2ky_2$$

where $y_1 = x_1 - \bar{x}_1$, $y_2 = x_2 - \bar{x}_2$.

Thus we have the normal *second-order* system

$$D^2 \begin{bmatrix} y_1 \\ y_2 \end{bmatrix} = k \begin{bmatrix} -\dfrac{2}{m_1} & \dfrac{1}{m_1} \\ \dfrac{1}{m_2} & -\dfrac{2}{m_2} \end{bmatrix} \begin{bmatrix} y_1 \\ y_2 \end{bmatrix}$$

which can be solved simply and directly using the methods of sub-section 13.2.2. The reduction to first-order is essential only when d_1 or d_2 is non-zero so that there are some lower order derivatives.

(ix) *lines 8 and 9, page* S263 These frequencies can be obtained by putting $\mu_1 = \mu_2 = \mu = \dfrac{1}{m}$ in the formula for λ^2 half-way down page S261.

Exercises

1. Evaluate $|A - \lambda I|$ for the matrix A on page S260 and hence obtain the eigenvectors of A in terms of λ, for the case

   $$m_1 = m_2 = m > 0.$$
   $$d_1 = d_2 = d > 0.$$

2. Find the general solution of the system of equations (5-52) on page S259 under the conditions

   $$m_1 = m_2 = m > 0$$
   $$F_1(t) = F_2(t) = 0$$
   $$d_1 = d_2 = d > 0$$
   $$d^2 > 12km.$$

Solutions

1. With $\mu = \dfrac{1}{m}$, $|A - \lambda I|$ becomes in this case

   $$\begin{vmatrix} -\lambda & 0 & \mu & 0 \\ 0 & -\lambda & 0 & \mu \\ -2k & k & -(\lambda + d\mu) & 0 \\ k & -2k & 0 & -(\lambda + d\mu) \end{vmatrix}$$

   To evaluate $|A - \lambda I|$ we reduce it to triangular form by row operations. In the notation of *Unit M100 26, Linear Algebra III*, let

   $$R_3 \longmapsto -\lambda R_3 + 2k R_1 - k R_2$$
   $$R_4 \longmapsto -\lambda R_4 - k R_1 + 2k R_2$$

   Thus

   $$|A - \lambda I| = \lambda^{-2} \begin{vmatrix} -\lambda & 0 & \mu & 0 \\ 0 & -\lambda & 0 & \mu \\ 0 & 0 & \lambda(\lambda + d\mu) + 2k\mu & -k\mu \\ 0 & 0 & -k\mu & \lambda(\lambda + d\mu) + 2k\mu \end{vmatrix}$$

$$R_4 \longmapsto R_4 + \frac{k\mu}{\lambda(\lambda + d\mu) + 2k\mu} R_3$$

$$|A - \lambda I| = \lambda^{-2} \begin{vmatrix} -\lambda & 0 & \mu & 0 \\ 0 & -\lambda & 0 & \mu \\ 0 & 0 & \lambda(\lambda + d\mu) + 2k\mu & -k\mu \\ 0 & 0 & 0 & z \end{vmatrix}$$

where $z = \lambda(\lambda + d\mu) + 2k\mu - \dfrac{k^2\mu^2}{\lambda(\lambda + d\mu) + 2k\mu}$.

Hence $|A - \lambda I| = [\lambda(\lambda + d\mu) + 2k\mu]^2 - k^2\mu^2$.

From the above, the row reduced form of $A - \lambda I$ is

$$\begin{bmatrix} -\lambda & 0 & \mu & 0 \\ 0 & -\lambda & 0 & \mu \\ 0 & 0 & \lambda(\lambda + d\mu) + 2k\mu & -k\mu \\ 0 & 0 & 0 & z \end{bmatrix}$$

Hence, since $(A - \lambda I)\mathbf{E}_\lambda = \mathbf{0}$, we obtain

$$\mathbf{E}_\lambda = (k,\ \lambda^2 m + d\lambda + 2k,\ \lambda km,\ \lambda m(\lambda^2 m + d\lambda + 2k))$$

2. Using Exercise 1,

$$|A - \lambda I| = \left(\lambda^2 + \frac{d\lambda}{m} + \frac{k}{m}\right)\left(\lambda^2 + \frac{d\lambda}{m} + \frac{3k}{m}\right).$$

Hence

$$\lambda_1, \lambda_2 = (-d \pm \sqrt{d^2 - 4km})/2m$$
$$\lambda_3, \lambda_4 = (-d \pm \sqrt{d^2 - 12km})/2m$$

Thus, since $d^2 > 12km$ all the eigenvalues are real, negative and distinct. Thus the problem falls into the class we discussed in sub-section 13.2.1. Corresponding eigenvectors are

$$\mathbf{E}_1 = (k,\ k,\ \lambda_1 km,\ \lambda_1 km)$$
$$\mathbf{E}_2 = (k,\ k,\ \lambda_2 km,\ \lambda_2 km)$$
$$\mathbf{E}_3 = (k,\ -k,\ \lambda_3 km,\ -\lambda_3 km)$$
$$\mathbf{E}_4 = (k,\ -k,\ \lambda_4 km,\ -\lambda_4 km)$$

From page S260

$$y_3 = m\dot{y}_1$$
$$y_4 = m\dot{y}_2$$

hence we only require y_1 and y_2:

$$y_1(t) = c_1 e^{\lambda_1 t} + c_2 e^{\lambda_2 t} + c_3 e^{\lambda_3 t} + c_4 e^{\lambda_4 t}$$
$$y_2(t) = c_1 e^{\lambda_1 t} + c_2 e^{\lambda_2 t} - c_3 e^{\lambda_3 t} - c_4 e^{\lambda_4 t}.$$

(Note that we have absorbed a common factor of k into the arbitrary constants.) Since each λ_i is negative $\lim_{t\ \text{large}} y_1(t)$ and $\lim_{t\ \text{large}} y_2(t)$ are zero: i.e. in the long run damping brings the system to rest.

13.3.2   Electrical Networks

In this final sub-section we return to a physical situation that we have met before: electrical networks. In problems involving networks each possible circuit has a current and the situation is described by a system of differential equations. We will not attempt to solve any equations in this sub-section but will concentrate on setting up such systems of equations.

READ Example 2 on page S263 as far as line −6, the sentence in brackets.

Notes

(i)   *line −13 page* S263 "applied electromotive force" means applied voltage.
(ii)   *line −10, page* S263 *et seq.* For Kirchhoff's laws, see page K170. To obtain the differential equations we consider
(a)   the *R-L-L-E* circuit, and
(b)   the *R-L-C* circuit
and use the form of the voltage drops given on pages K170 and 172.
To reduce the system to normal form we first eliminate *di/dt* from the first equation, obtaining

$$L\frac{di_1}{dt} = -\frac{1}{C}q_2 + E(t).$$

i.e.

$$\frac{di_1}{dt} = -\frac{1}{LC}q_2 + \frac{E(t)}{L}$$

$$\frac{di}{dt} = -\frac{Ri}{L} + \frac{1}{LC}q_2$$

We then note that $i_2 = i_1 - i$ (applying Kirchhoff's first law to either node of the network), so that

$$\frac{dq_2}{dt} = i_1 - i$$

You should note that it is convenient to use the currents i_r as the unknown functions *except* for wires containing a condenser in which case the corresponding i should be replaced by $\frac{dq}{dt}$.

READ Example 3 on page S265.

The two circuits considered here are the R_1-R_2-L-E circuit and the R_2-C circuit. In normal form the equations may be written

$$\begin{bmatrix} \dfrac{di_1}{dt} \\ \dfrac{di_3}{dt} \end{bmatrix} = \begin{bmatrix} -\dfrac{R_1}{L} & -\dfrac{R_2}{L} \\ \dfrac{1}{R_2C} & -\dfrac{1}{R_2C} \end{bmatrix}\begin{bmatrix} i_1 \\ i_3 \end{bmatrix} + \begin{bmatrix} \dfrac{1}{L}E(t) \\ 0 \end{bmatrix}$$

In this form the system is incomplete: there is also the additional equation $\frac{dq_2}{dt} = i_1 - i_3$.

Exercise

Consider the following network and write down a normal system of equations which describes its behaviour.

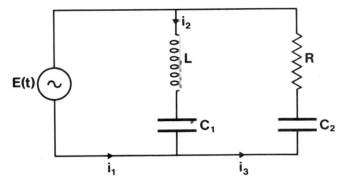

Solution

For the E-L-C_1 circuit we have

$$\frac{q_2}{C_1} + L\frac{di_2}{dt} = E(t), \qquad i_2 = \frac{dq_2}{dt}.$$

For the C_2-R-E circuit we have

$$\frac{q_3}{C_2} + i_3 R = E(t), \qquad i_3 = \frac{dq_3}{dt}.$$

Because we have a condenser and an inductance in the same wire, it is necessary to use both i_2 and q_2 as unknowns. We use q_3 as the third unknown. The system is

$$\frac{di_2}{dt} = -\frac{q_2}{LC_1} + \frac{1}{L}E(t)$$

$$\frac{dq_2}{dt} = i_2$$

$$\frac{dq_3}{dt} = -\frac{q_3}{RC_2} + \frac{1}{R}E(t)$$

In addition $i_1 = \frac{dq_3}{dt} - i_2$, but this equation does not appear in the system since $\frac{di_1}{dt}$ does not appear.

13.3.3 Summary of Section 13.3

In this section no new theory was developed. We modelled a mass-spring system and electrical networks, expressing the systems of differential equations in normal form.

13.4 Summary of the Unit

In this unit we developed a way of solving directly a system of differential equations.

In the first section we discussed the structure of a system of differential equations and what is meant by the normal form of such a system. We restricted ourselves to the first-order case for there are many higher order systems which can be made equivalent to first order systems. The last two sub-sections considered the existence of solutions to the system and the nature of the resulting solution space. The second section developed a method for solving constant-coefficient homogeneous systems. The steps are summarized in the form of a flow chart at the end of that section. The last section then applied the theory learnt to two particular physical systems: a double mass spring system and electric circuits.

Definitions

system of linear differential equations	(page S224)	★ ★ ★
homogeneous system	(page S224)	★ ★
nonhomogeneous system	(page S224)	★ ★
operator matrix	(page S224)	★ ★
normal first-order system	(page S225)	★ ★
Wronskian	(page C10)	★ ★

Theorems

1. **(Theorem 5-11, page S228)**
Let

$$\mathbf{X}' = A(t)\mathbf{X} + \mathbf{B}(t)$$

be a normal $n \times n$-first-order system of linear differential equations defined on an interval I. Then if t_0 is any point in I and $\mathbf{X}_0$ is any vector in $\mathscr{R}^n$, the given system has a unique solution $\mathbf{X} = \mathbf{X}(t)$ such that $\mathbf{X}(t_0) = \mathbf{X}_0$.   ★ ★ ★

2. **(Initial Condition Isomorphism Theorem, page C8)**
Let $\mathcal{W}$ be the solution set of $\mathbf{X}'(t) = A(t)\mathbf{X}(t) + \mathbf{B}(t)$, $t \in I$, and let   ★ ★ ★
$E: \mathcal{W} \longrightarrow \mathscr{R}^n$ be specified by $E(\mathbf{X}) = \mathbf{X}(t_0)$, $t_0 \in I$. Then E is one-to-one and onto.

3. **(Theorem 5-12, page S229)**
The dimension of the solution space $\mathcal{W}$ of any homogeneous $n \times n$-system   ★ ★
$\mathbf{X}' = A(t)\mathbf{X}$ is n, the number of equations in the system.

4. **(Lemma 5-3, page S251)**
For each real eigenvalue λ of A and each eigenvector   ★

$$\mathbf{E}_\lambda = \begin{bmatrix} e_1 \\ \vdots \\ e_n \end{bmatrix}$$

belonging to λ, the function $\mathbf{X}_\lambda = \mathbf{E}_\lambda e^{\lambda t}$ is a solution of $\mathbf{X}' = A\mathbf{X}$. Moreover, solutions formed in this way from distinct eigenvalues are linearly independent in $\mathcal{V}_n$.

5. **(Corollary 5-3, page S251)**
If A has n distinct real eigenvalues $\lambda_1, \ldots, \lambda_n$ and if $\mathbf{E}_{\lambda_1}, \ldots, \mathbf{E}_{\lambda_n}$ are   ★
eigenvectors belonging to these eigenvalues, then the general solution of the normal first-order system $\mathbf{X}' = A\mathbf{X}$ is

$$\mathbf{X}(t) = c_1 \mathbf{E}_{\lambda_1} e^{\lambda_1 t} + \ldots, + c_n \mathbf{E}_{\lambda_n} e^{\lambda_n t},$$

where $c_1, \ldots, c_n$ are arbitrary constants.

6. **(Theorem, page C14)**
If the eigenvectors $\mathbf{E}_1, \ldots, \mathbf{E}_n$ of an $n \times n$ matrix A form a basis for R^n,   ★ ★ ★
then the general solution of $\mathbf{X}' = A\mathbf{X}$ is $\mathbf{X}(t) = c_1 \mathbf{E}_1 e^{\lambda_1 t} + \cdots + c_n \mathbf{E}_n e^{\lambda_n t}$,
where $\mathbf{E}_i$ is an eigenvector corresponding to λ_i.

7. (**Lemma 5-4**, page S253)
Let A be an $n \times n$ matrix with real entries, and suppose that $\lambda = \alpha + \beta i$ is an eigenvalue for A. Then if $\mathbf{Z}$ is an eigenvector belonging to λ, $\overline{\mathbf{Z}}$, the complex conjugate of $\mathbf{Z}$, is an eigenvector belonging to $\overline{\lambda} = \alpha - \beta i$.

    ★ ★

8. (**Lemma 5-5**, page S254)
Let A be a real $n \times n$-matrix, and suppose that $\mathbf{E}_\lambda$ is an eigenvector in $\mathbb{C}^n$ belonging to the complex eigenvalue $\lambda = \alpha + \beta i$ of A. Then

    ★

$$\mathbf{E}_\lambda e^{\lambda t} \quad \text{and} \quad \overline{\mathbf{E}}_\lambda e^{\overline{\lambda} t}$$

are solutions of the equation $\mathbf{X}' = A\mathbf{X}$.

9. (**Lemma 5-6**, page S255)
Let $\lambda = \alpha + \beta i$ be a complex eigenvalue for the $n \times n$ real matrix A, and let $\mathbf{E}_\lambda$ be an eigenvector in $\mathbb{C}^n$ belonging to λ. Then the functions

    ★ ★

$$\mathbf{X}_1(t) = e^{\alpha t}(\mathbf{G}_\lambda \cos \beta t + \mathbf{H}_\lambda \sin \beta t)$$
$$\mathbf{X}_2(t) = e^{\alpha t}(\mathbf{H}_\lambda \cos \beta t - \mathbf{G}_\lambda \sin \beta t)$$

where $\mathbf{G}_\lambda = \dfrac{\mathbf{E}_\lambda + \overline{\mathbf{E}}_\lambda}{2}$ and $\mathbf{H}_\lambda = \dfrac{i(\mathbf{E}_\lambda - \overline{\mathbf{E}}_\lambda)}{2}$ are linearly independent solutions of $\mathbf{X}' = A\mathbf{X}$.

Techniques

1. Given a system of first-order linear differential equations, put it into normal form.

    ★ ★

2. Solve a normal system of equations $\mathbf{X}' = A\mathbf{X}$ where A is a matrix of real constants. (See the summary of Section 13.2.)

    ★ ★

3. Derive a system of equations for a mass-spring system, and an electrical network

    ★ ★ ★

Notation

$\mathbf{X}$	(page S224)
$\mathcal{V}_n$	(page S225)
E	(page C8)
E_t	(page C10)
$W[\mathbf{X}_1, \ldots, \mathbf{X}_n]$	(page C10)
$\mathbf{E}_\lambda$	(page S251)
$\mathbf{X}_\lambda$	(page S251)
$\mathbf{E}_\lambda^{(i)}$	(page C14)
$\mathbf{G}_\lambda$	(page S255)
$\mathbf{H}_\lambda$	(page S255)

13.5   SELF-ASSESSMENT

Self-assessment Test

This Self-assessment Test is designed to help you test quickly your understanding of the unit. It can also be used, together with the summary of the unit for revision. The answers to these questions will be found on the next non-facing page. We suggest you complete the whole test before looking at the answers.

1.   Write the differential equation

$$D^4 y(x) + x D^2 y(x) + 4 y(x) = \cos x$$

as a normal first-order system of equations in matrix form.

2.   Reduce the following system of equations to a normal first-order system in matrix form

$$4 D y_1(x) + 6 y_1(x) + D y_2(x) = e^x$$
$$2 y_2(x) + D y_1(x) - 3 D y_2(x) = e^{-x}$$

3.   Solve the system of equations $\mathbf{X}' = A\mathbf{X}$, where

$A = \begin{bmatrix} 1 & 1 \\ 2 & 3 \end{bmatrix}$ with initial condition $\mathbf{X}(0) = (0, 1)$.

4.   Consider the following network and find a normal first-order system of equations which describe its behaviour.

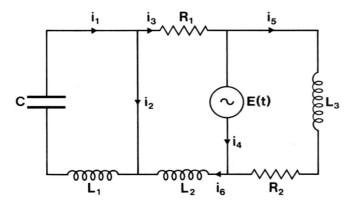

Solutions to Self-assessment Test

1. $\mathbf{Y}'(x) = \begin{bmatrix} 0 & 1 & 0 & 0 \\ 0 & 0 & 1 & 0 \\ 0 & 0 & 0 & 1 \\ -4 & 0 & -x & 0 \end{bmatrix} \mathbf{Y}(x) + \begin{bmatrix} 0 \\ 0 \\ 0 \\ \cos x \end{bmatrix}$

2. First treat $Dy_1(x)$ and $Dy_2(x)$ as algebraic unknowns.

$$\begin{bmatrix} 4 & 1 \\ 1 & -3 \end{bmatrix} \begin{bmatrix} Dy_1(x) \\ Dy_2(x) \end{bmatrix} = \begin{bmatrix} -6y_1(x) + e^x \\ -2y_2(x) + e^{-x} \end{bmatrix}$$

$$R_1 \longmapsto 3R_1 + R_2$$
$$R_2 \longmapsto R_2 - \tfrac{1}{13}R_1$$

$$\begin{bmatrix} 13 & 0 \\ 0 & -3 \end{bmatrix} \begin{bmatrix} Dy_1(x) \\ Dy_2(x) \end{bmatrix}$$

$$= \begin{bmatrix} -18y_1(x) - 2y_2(x) + 3e^x + e^{-x} \\ \tfrac{18}{13}y_1(x) - \tfrac{24}{13}y_2(x) - \tfrac{3}{13}e^x + \tfrac{12}{13}e^{-x} \end{bmatrix}$$

Rearranging

$$\begin{bmatrix} Dy_1(x) \\ Dy_2(x) \end{bmatrix} = \begin{bmatrix} -\tfrac{18}{13} & -\tfrac{2}{13} \\ -\tfrac{6}{13} & \tfrac{8}{13} \end{bmatrix} \begin{bmatrix} y_1(x) \\ y_2(x) \end{bmatrix} + \tfrac{1}{13} \begin{bmatrix} 3e^x + e^{-x} \\ e^x - 4e^{-\lambda} \end{bmatrix}$$

3.

$$\begin{vmatrix} 1-\lambda & 1 \\ 2 & 3-\lambda \end{vmatrix} = 3 - 4\lambda + \lambda^2 - 2 = \lambda^2 - 4\lambda + 1 = 0$$

i.e. $\lambda = 2 \pm \sqrt{4-1}$

$\qquad = 2 \pm \sqrt{3}.$

Eigenvectors are

$$\mathbf{E}_\lambda = \begin{bmatrix} -1 \\ 1-\lambda \end{bmatrix}$$

i.e.

$$\mathbf{E}_{2+\sqrt{3}} = (-1, -1-\sqrt{3})$$
$$\mathbf{E}_{2-\sqrt{3}} = (-1, -1+\sqrt{3})$$

Therefore the general solution is

$$c_1(-1, -1-\sqrt{3})e^{(2+\sqrt{3})t} + c_2(-1, -1+\sqrt{3})e^{(2-\sqrt{3})t}$$

Since $\mathbf{X}(0) = (0, 1)$, we have $c_1 + c_2 = 0$

$$-c_1 - \sqrt{3}c_1 - c_2 + \sqrt{3}c_2 = 1$$

i.e.

$$c_2 - c_1 = \frac{1}{\sqrt{3}}$$

$$c_1 = -\frac{1}{2\sqrt{3}}, \quad c_2 = \frac{1}{2\sqrt{3}}.$$

Solution is:

$$\frac{e^{2t}}{2\sqrt{3}}\{(1, 1+\sqrt{3})e^{\sqrt{3}t} + (-1, -1+\sqrt{3})e^{-\sqrt{3}t}\}$$

4. Use (i) C-L_1 circuit
 (ii) L_2-E-R_1 circuit
 (iii) L_3-R_2-E circuit

(i) $\dfrac{q_1}{C} + L_1 \dfrac{di_1}{dt} = 0 \qquad i_1 = \dfrac{dq_1}{dt}$

(ii) $L_2 \dfrac{di_6}{dt} + i_3 R_1 = E(t)$

(iii) $L_3 \dfrac{di_5}{dt} + i_5 R_2 = E(t)$

By Kirchhoff's first law: $i_3 = i_1 - i_2 = i_1 - (i_1 - i_6) = i_6$

In normal form we have

$$\frac{dq_1}{dt} = i_1$$

$$\frac{di_1}{dt} = \frac{-q_1}{L_1 C}$$

$$\frac{di_5}{dt} = -\frac{R_2}{L_3} i_5 + \frac{E(t)}{L_3}$$

$$\frac{di_6}{dt} = -\frac{R_1}{L_2} i_6 + \frac{E(t)}{L_3}$$

Other solutions are possible.

LINEAR MATHEMATICS